INTERNATIONAL STANDARD BOOK No: 0-948964-30-8   1
(changes wi+h ᵃⁿᵃᵇ ᵃ-ᵈᵐ '

Commemorating the GOLDEN JUBI

COLLECTORS' C(

by R. J

30th Editio

from 1820 in rising order of face-value

QUARTER-FARTHINGS to CROWNS
DECIMAL CENT to FIVE POUNDS

Copper, Bronze, Silver, Nickel-brass and Cupro-nickel
EVERY non-gold coin from 1820 separately listed for:

GEORGE IV	House of HANOVER	1820 -	1830
WILLIAM IV	House of HANOVER	1830 -	1837
VICTORIA	House of HANOVER	1837 -	1901
EDWARD VII	SAXE-COBURG	1901 -	1910
GEORGE V	House of WINDSOR	1910 -	1936
EDWARD VIII	House of WINDSOR	1936	
GEORGE VI	House of WINDSOR	1936 -	1952
ELIZABETH II	House of WINDSOR	1952 to date	

ONE HUNDRED and EIGHTY THREE YEARS

Photographs of coins, and information extracted from its reports,
are reproduced with the permission of the Royal Mint.

A compilation of averaged selling-prices drawn from
dealers' lists, auctions and numismatic magazines.

ROTOGRAPHIC · 320 Lichfield Avenue · Barton · Torquay · TQ2 8AH

2 QUARTER FARTHINGS FOR USE IN CEYLON

Date	Mintage		Fair/Fine		V.F.	E.F.	Unc/abt.FDC

VICTORIA YOUNG HEAD — COPPER 13.5mm

Date	Mintage		Fair/Fine		V.F.	E.F.	Unc/abt.FDC
1839	3,840,000	£10		£18	£35		£55/£75
1851	Included below	£12		£20	£40		£65/£95
1852	2,215,000	£10		£18	£35		£60/£90
1853	Included above	£6/£10		£20	£40		£65/£95
1853	Bronzed proofs	(from the sets)			- - -		£250
1853	Cupro-nickel proofs (P1615)				- - -		£500/£700
1868	Bronze proofs	(P1616)			- - -		£250
1868	Bronze proofs	(noted 1999)			"FDC"		£350

THIRD FARTHINGS FOR USE IN MALTA

GEORGE IV — COPPER 16mm

Date		Fair/Fine		V.F.	E.F.	Unc/abt.FDC
1827		£6	£15	£40		£60/£80
1827	Proof	- - -	- -	£45		£175/£200

WILLIAM IV — COPPER 16mm

Date		Fair/Fine		V.F.	E.F.	Unc/abt.FDC
1835		£4	£16	£40		£60/£80
1835	(noted 2000)	"BU Full Lustre"				£125/- - -
1835	Proof	- - -	- - -	- - -		£175/- - -

VICTORIA YOUNG HEAD — COPPER · 16mm

Date		Fair/Fine		V.F.	E.F.	Unc/abt.FDC
1844	1,301,040	£20	£35	£75		£90/£150
1844	RE for REG (P1607)	£100	£250	£750		£950/£1200
1844	Large 'G'	£20	£50	£95		£150/£250

"BUN" HEAD — BRONZE · 16mm

Date	Mintage	Fair/Fine		V.F.	E.F.	Unc/abt.FDC
1866	576,000	£3	£5	£10		£20/£30
1868	144,000	£1/£4	£5	£12		£25/£40
1868	Proof in cupro-nickel	- - -	- - -			£200
1868	Proof in aluminium	- - -	- - -			£450
1876	162,000	£1/£4	£8	£16		£30/£45
1878	288,000	£3	£5	£10		£20/£30
1881	144,000	£3	£5	£10		£20/£30
1884	144,000	£3	£5	£12		£20/£30
1885	288,000	£3	£5	£10		£20/£30

Proofs: 1866 £175; 1868 £200; 1881 £200

EDWARD VII — BRONZE 15mm

Date		Fair/Fine	V.F.	E.F.	Unc/abt.FDC
1902	288,000	£1	£3	£6	£10/£15
1902	(noted 1990 Seaby)	- - -		"abt. Unc" £6	

GEORGE V — BRONZE 15mm

Date		Fair/Fine	V.F.	E.F.	Unc/abt.FDC
1913	288,000	£1	£3	£6	£10/£15

HALF FARTHINGS FOR USE IN CEYLON

GEORGE IV LAUREATE HEAD — COPPER 18mm

Date	Mintage		Fair/Fine	V.F.	E.F.	Unc/abt.FDC
1828	7,680,000	Rev A	£10	£20	£75	£120/£200
1828	Rev B see below	£15	£30	£150		£225/£350
1828	Proof	- - -	- - -	- - -		£250
1828	Bronzed proof	- - -	- - -	- - -		£500
1830	8,776,320	£20	£50	£150		£250/£325
1830	Smaller date	£8	£15	£75		£120/£200
1830	Rev B see below	£20	£60	£200		£300/£450

Rev A: trident reaches above base of letters
Rev B: the trident reaches base of letters

Date	Mintage	Peck	Fine	V.F.	E.F.	abt Unc/FDC

WILLIAM IV

COPPER 18mm

Date	Mintage	Peck	Fine	V.F.	E.F.	abt Unc/FDC
1837	1,935,360		£40	£90	£200	£400/£500

VICTORIA YOUNG HEAD

COPPER 18mm

Date	Mintage	Peck	Fine	V.F.	E.F.	abt Unc/FDC
1839	2,042,880		£5	£10	£30	£50/£70
1839	Proof bronsed		- -	- -	- -	£200
1842			£4	£10	£25	£45/£65
1843	3,440,640		£2	£6	£16	£30/£50
1844	6,451,000		£2	£5	£10	£20/£40
1844	E of REGINA over N		£10	£20	£40	£120/£250
1847	3,010,560		£4	£6	£20	£40/£60
1851	Unknown	P1597	£4	£10	£25	£50/£70
1851	1 struck over 5		£5	£12	£30	£70/£100
1851	5 struck over blundered number		- -		£95	- - - / - - -
1852	989,184		£6	£12	£30	£60/£80
1853	955,224		£8	£20	£60	£140/£225
1853	Copper proof		- -	- -	FDC	£250
1853	Bronzed proof		- -	- -	FDC	£300
1854	677,376		£10	£20	£50	£100/£175
1856	913,920	P1603	£12	£30	£75	£150/£225
1856	(noted 1995)		"Superb BU full lustre"			£250
1856	Large date		£20	£40 (not distinguished in Peck)		
1868	Bronze proof P1605		(noted 1999) "Virt FDC"			£425
1868	Cupro-nickel proof		(noted 1999) "Virt FDC"			£435

FARTHINGS

Date	Mintage	Peck No.	Fine	V.F.	E.F.	abt. Unc/FDC

GEORGE IV

Laureate Head DATE BELOW BRITTANIA · COPPER 22mm

Date	Mintage	Peck No.	Fine	V.F.	E.F.	abt. Unc/FDC
1821	2,688,000 Obv.1	P1407	£2	£9	£18	£50/£70
1821	G of GRATIA over O (Colin Cooke mint 1994)				"Mint state" £69	
1821	Proof in copper	P1408	- - -	(noted 1999)	"FDC"	£380
1822	5,924,352 Obv.1	P1409	£2	£8	£20	£50/£70
1822	Proof in copper		- - -	- - -	- - -	£350/- - -
1822	Obverse 2	P1411	£1	£3	£10	£20/£40
1822	"Doubled" D in DEF.		(noted 2001)		"Unc."	£36
1823	2,365,440	P1412	£3	£9	£25	£50/£75
1823	Date has I for 1		£5	£20	£40	£65/£95
1825	4,300,800 Obv.1	P1414	£2	£4	£10	£20/£40
1825	5 over 3 (Noted 1993)		£25	- - -	£45	- - - / - - -
1825	D of DEI over U		£10	£50	£120	- - - / - - -
1825	Obverse 2	P1414A	£4	£8	£20	£50/£75
1825	Proof in gold	P1415	- - -	- - -	Coincraft Cat. £4,000	
1826	6,666,240	P1416	£3	£10	£30	£60/£80

4 FARTHINGS

GEORGE IV

Undraped or Bare Head   DATE BELOW HEAD · COPPER 22mm

Date	Mintage	Peck No.	Fine	V.F.	E.F.	abt. Unc/FDC
1826	Inc. above	P1439	£2	£6	£25	£50/£75
1826	I for 1	(noted 1995)	£80	- - -	- - -	£350/- - -
1826	I for 1	(noted 1999)	"Choice EF"		£195	- - -/- - -
1826	I for 1	(noted 2000)	"VF" £145		£195	- - -/- - -
1826	Bronzed Proof	P1440	- - -	- - -	FDC	£160
1826	Copper Proof	P1441	- - -	- - -	£60	- - -/- - -
1827	2,365,440	P1442	£3	£9	£30	£65/£90
1828	2,365,440	P1443	£3	£9	£25	£60/£85
1829	1,505,280	P1444	£3	£12	£45	£95/- - -
1830	2,365,440	P1445	£4	£8	£20	£60/£85
1830	(noted 1999)		- - -	- - -	"Superb FDC"	£125

All dies are punched more than once. If one blow fails to register with another, then figures appear doubled, even trebled: this is very common. A major misalignment, however, will add value to the coin.

Obverse 1: Peck says 'the leaf-midribs (if present) are single raised lines'
Obverse 2: The 3 lowest leaves have incuse midribs.

Patterns versus Proofs · If the currency which follows differs then the pattern remains as such. If, however, the currency is based on the pattern then the pattern becomes a proof of that currency. The pattern is a "loner", the proof has "friends".

WILLIAM IV

DATE BELOW HEAD · COPPER 22mm

Date	Mintage	Peck No.	Fine	V.F.	E.F.	abt. Unc/FDC
1831	2,688,000	P1466	£3	£8	£25	£50/£75
1831	Proof	P1467	- - - -	bronzed		£180/£250
1831	Proof	P1468	inverted reverse			- - -/£150
1831	Proof	P1468	(noted 1999)		"FDC"	£175
1831	Proof	P1469	- - - -	copper		- - -/£375
1834	1,935,360 Rev.A	P1470	£2	£10	£30	£50/£75
1834	Reverse B	P1471	£2	£6	£25	£60/£95
1835	1,720,320 Rev.A	P1472	£2	£6	£30	£60/£95
1835	Reverse B	P1473	£2	£10	£30	£50/£75
1836	1,290,240	P1474	£3	£6	£25	£60/£95
1837	3,010,560	P1475	£5	£10	£40	£80/£125
1837	7 struck over blundered figure		£10	£20	£60	£120/- - - -

Reverse B has raised line down the arms of saltire
(cross of St.Andrew) (see page 17); whereas Reverse A has incuse line

Date	Mintage	Peck No.	Fine	V.F.	E.F.	abt. Unc/FDC
VICTORIA	**YOUNG HEAD**			DATE BELOW HEAD · COPPER 22mm		
1838	591,360 DEF.	P1553	£5	£10	£25	£45/£65
1838	Variety DEF : on	P1553	£6	£12	£30	£65/---
1839	4,300,800 DEF.	P1554	£3	£6	£18	£40/£65
1839	(no stop) DEF	P1554	£4	£8	£20	£40/£65
1839	Proofs in copper		---	---	---	---/---
1839	Proofs in bronzed copper		---	---	---	---/£180
1839	Two pronged trident (a 'bident'?)			£6	£18	£40/£60
1840	3,010,560	P1559	£3	£6	£18	£40/£60
1840	Variety DEF.. on	P1559	£4	£8	£25	---/---
1841	1,720,320	P1560	£4	£8	£20	£40/£60
1841	Varieties P1560	REG. and REG for REG:			£30	£60/£90
1841	Proof	P1561				£800/£1000
1842	1,290,240	P1562	£10	£25	£75	£100/£150
1842	Variety on P1562		£10 (large '42' in date)			---/---
1843	Struck over 1842		---	---	---	---/---
1843	4,085,760	P1563	£3	£7	£18	£35/£60
1843	I for 1 in date		£25	£50	£150	£300/---
1844	430,080	P1565	£40	£95	£250	£500/£1000
1844	(At auction 1987)	"Mint state"			---	£836
1845	3,225,600	P1566	£3	£6	£18	£40/£65
1845	Large date	"F/gdF"	£55		(Colin Cooke 1996)	
1846	2,580,480	P1567	£8	£16	£50	£75/£125
1847	3,879,720	P1568	£2	£6	£18	£40/£60
1847	Proof		--	--	---	---/---
1848	1,290,246	P1569	£3	£6	£18	£40/£60
1849	645,120	P1570	£10	£30	£60	£120/£225
1850	430,080 ?	P1571	£2	£5	£20	£40/£60
1850	5 over inverted 5	؟	---	---	---	---/---
	possibly, 5 over damaged 5 (no upright stroke) and much like a 3					
1850	5 over 4 (noted 1999)	"nrEF"		£35	"Unc"	£120/---
1851	1,935,360	P1572	£10	£20	£50	£95/£150
1851	D of DEI STRUCK OVER ▽		--	£200	£400	£625/----
1852	822,528	P1574	£10	£20	£50	---/----
1852	(noted 1999)	"Almost Unc good lustre"				£175
1853	1,028,628 : W.W. raised	P1575	£1	£3	£10	£25/£50
1853	3 struck over 2	raised W.W.		---	---	£45/£70
1853	Proof, bronzed, with inverted reverse			---	---	---/---
1853	Proof with raised W.W.	P1577		---	---	£250/£350
1853	WW incuse	P1578	£4	£8	£20	£40/£60
1853	Proof with incuse WW	P1579	from the sets			£200/£300
1854	6,504,960	P1580	£2	£5	£10	£30/£60
1855	3,440,640	WW incuse P1581	£10	£25	£55/£90	
1855	Included	W.W. raised P1582	£15	£40	£75/£125	

6   FARTHINGS   abt.

Date	Mintage	Peck No.	Fine	V.F.	E.F.	Unc/FDC

VICTORIA YOUNG HEAD   DATE BELOW HEAD · COPPER 22mm

Date	Mintage	Peck No.	Fine	V.F.	E.F.	Unc/FDC
1856	1,771,392	P1583	£5	£10	£20	£45/£90
★1856	E over R (VICTORIA)	P1584	£15	£80	- - -	- - -/- - -
1857	1,075,200	P1585	£5	£10	£25	£50/£75
1858	1,720,320	P1586	£5	£10	£25	£50/£75
1858	(noted 1998) "BU Full Lustre, exceptional"					£110
1858	Small date		£15	£25	£50	- - -/- - -
1859	1,290,240	P1587	£15	£30	£60	£100/£150
1860	Obverse date currency			C. Cooke 1990 abt Unc £3900		
1860	Obverse date proof			C. Cooke 1990 abt Unc £3600		
1864	(Cooke 1993)	P1589		Colin not selling even at £7,500!		

★ 1856 Also described as R over E. Either R was struck over an incorrect
E, or E was wrongly selected to improve a poor R; (or ?): reads VICTOEIA.

DATE BELOW BRITANNIA · BRONZE 20mm

VICTORIA BUN HEAD   BRONZE = Copper 95% · Tin 4% · Zinc 1%

BB = Border of Beads   TB = Toothed Border

Date	Mintage	Peck No.	Fine	V.F.	E.F.	Unc/FDC
1860	2,867,200 with various "Berries-in-Wreath" obverses:					
1860	BB 3 berries	P1854	£2	£5	£10	£20/£30
1860	Proof	P1856	- - -	- - -	- - -	£175
1860	MULE combining beaded and toothed borders:					
		P1857	£100	£200	£400	£1200/- - -
1860	TB 4 berries	P1858	£1	£2	£5	£10/£20
1860	Bronze proof		- - -	- - -	- - -	£200/£300
1860	TB 5 berries	P1859	£1	£3	£6	£18/£25
1860	(noted 1996)	P1859	- - -	"Full lustre"		£26
1861	8,601,600 4 berries	P1860	£1	£2	£8	£16/£24
1861	Bronze proof (Cooke 1998)		- - -	"FDC"		- - -/£235
1861	Obv. 3 (5 berries)		£1	£2	£6	£12/£20
1861	Date has small '8'		£2	£4	£12	£25/- - -
1862	14,336,000	P1865	£1	£3	£18	£35/£50
1862	Proof		- - -	- - -	£200	- - -/- - -
1862	Large 8 over small 8		(1990)		£30	- - -/- - -
1863	1,433,600	P1867	£20	£45	£75	£150/£300
1864	2,508,800 serif 4	P1869	£2	£6	£10	£20/£40
1864	plain 4		- - -	£9	£15	£30/£50
1865	4,659,200	P1873	£2	£5	£15	£25/£35
1865	5 over 2	P1872A	£3	£8	£20	£40/£75
1865	5 over 3		£4	£8	£20	£35/£55
1865	Date has small '8'		£2	£8	£16	£32/- - -
1866	3,584,000	P1875	£1	£3	£12	£20/£30
1866	widely spaced 6s		£1	£3	£9	£18/£30
1867	5,017,600	P1878	£1	£3	£8	£18/£35
1867	Bronzed copper proof	P1879		- - -	"FDC"	£325
1868	4,851,208	P1881	£1	£3	£8	£18/£35
1868	Bronze proof	P1882	- - -	- - -	- - -	£145/£250
1868	Cu-nickel proof	P1883	- - -	- - -	"FDC"	£425
1869	3,225,600	P1884	£2	£6	£22	£40/£65
1872	2,150,400	P1885	£1	£3	£6	£20/£30
1873	3,225,620	P1886	£1	£2	£5	£15/£25
1873	Low set 3 in date		£1	£5	£10	£20/£36

Proofs also occur for 1861, 1862, 1863, 1866.

VICTORIA

Date	Mintage	Peck No.	Fine	V.F.	E.F.	ebt. Unc/FDC

OBVERSE 4 'AGED' (MATRONLY) BUST still 'BUN HEAD
'H' (centred below date) = Heaton Mint

Date	Mintage	Peck No.	Fine	V.F.	E.F.	Unc/FDC
1874H	3,584,000	P1887	£2	£5	£15	£30/£45
1874H	Bronze proof	(noted 1999)			"about FDC"	---/£180
1874H	Gs struck over ᑲ ᑲ		£50	£125	£250	£450/£650
1875	712,760	P1890	£10	£20	£50	£85/£110
1875	8 struck over 8		---	---	---	---/---
1875	Large date	(5 berries)	£5	£12	£25	£65/£95
1875	Small date	(5 berries)	£6	£22	£45	£125/£300
1875	Small dates	(4 berries)	£10	£25	£50	£175/£350
1975H	6,092,800	P1892	25p	£2	£8	£60/£100
1875H	(noted 1999)	5 over 2	---	---	£50	---/---
1975H	RF.G for REG		£1	£3	£6	£20/£30
1876H	1,175,200	P1894	£5	£10	£30	£60/£100
1876H	Large 6 in date		£10	£25	£60	£100/----
1876H	RF.G for REG		£5	£15	£60	£120/----
1877	Proofs only	P1895	bronze	(Cooke '98)		£2,250
1878	4,008,540	P1898	£1	£2	£10	£20/£30
1678	(exaggerated) date spacing variety		---	---		---/---
1878	Proof	P1897	---	---	---	---/£325
1879	3,977,180	P1898	£1	£2	£10	£20/£30
1879	Date has large '9'		£1	£5	£15	£35/£50
1880	1,842,710	P1899 (4 berries)		£5	£20	£40/£60
1880	(3 berries)	P1901	£10	£40	£60	£100/----
1881	Obv. 4 (incl. below) P1901A		£20	£35	£70	£95/£150
1881	3,494,670 Obv. 5	P1902	£1	£3	£10	£29/£45
1881	Colin Cooke lists seven "easily determined" varieties of Obverse 5					
1881H	1,792,000	P1904	£2	£5	£12	£25/£40
1882H	1,790,000	P1905	£2	£5	£12	£25/£40
1882H and 1883 have damaged die varieties						
1883	1,128,680	P1907	£2	£5	£20	£45/65
1884	5,782,000	P1909	£1	£2	£8	£20/£35
1885	5,442,308	P1911	£1	£2	£8	£20/£35
Proofs, in bronze, for all except 1876H and 1879						
1886	7,767,790	P1913	---	£1	£6	£12/£18
1887	1,340,800	P1915	£1	£3	£12	£24/£35
1888	1,887,250	P1916	£1	£2	£10	£20/£30
1890	2,133,070	P1917	£1	£2	£10	£20/£30
1891	4,959,690	P1919	£1	£2	£9	£18/£25
1892	887,240	P1921	£5	£10	£30	£60/£80
1893	3,904,320	P1923	£1	£2	£8	£16/£25
1893	Narrower date		£2	£5	£12	£25/£65
1894	2,396,770	P1924	£1	£3	£10	£20/£30
1895	2,852,853	P1925	£10	£20	£50	£100/£150

Proofs occur ecept for 1881H, 1887, 1888, 1893 and 1895

FARTHINGS

Date	Mintage	Peck No.	Fine	V.F.	E.F.	abt. Unc/ FDC

VICTORIA 'OLD' or WIDOW HEAD
COPPER 20mm

Date	Mintage	Peck No.	Fine	V.F.	E.F.	abt. Unc/ FDC
1895	Inc page7	P1958	50p	£2	£6	£12/£25
1896	3,668,610	P1559	50p	£2	£5	£10/£20
1896	(noted 2000)	"Full lustre, quite superb"		– – –		– – –/£20
1897	4,579,800:		blackened to distinguish from half-sovereign			
1897	Undarkened	P1961	£1	£3	£10	£20/£40
1897 ★	Horizon as	P1961 but black finish	£3	£10		£20/£40
1897★★	Higher horizon	P1962	£1	£3	£10	£20/£40
1898	4,010,080	P1965	50p	£2	£6	£12/£24
1899	3,864,616	P1964	50p	£1	£6	£12/£24
1900	5,969,317	P1965	50p	£1	£6	£12/£24
1901	8,016,459	P1966	50p	£1	£3	£9/£15

Proofs occur for 1896 and, possibly, for 1901

Obverse 4 (page 7) has 4 berries in wreath arranged as two pairs (2 + 2) not (1 + 2 + 1) as before. Obverse 5 has 3 berries arranged 2 + 1.

★ Rev A the '7' points TO a border tooth
★★ Rev B the '7' points BETWEEN two teeth

EDWARD VII
COPPER 20mm

Date	Mintage		Fine	V.F.	E.F.	abt. Unc/ FDC
1902	Type A · weak strike · patchy breastplate					
	Type B · well struck · clear design work					
1902	5,125,120	Type A	25p	£2	£8	£16/£25
1902	incl. above	Type B	25p	£1	£4	£8/£12
1903	5,331,200	low horizon	60p	£3	£6	£12/£20
1904	3,628,800		50p	£3	£7	£15/£20
1905	4,076,800		50p	£3	£7	£15/£20
1906	5,340,160		50p	£3	£7	£15/£20
1907	4,399,360		30p	£2	£6	£12/£18
1908	4,264,960		30p	£2	£6	£12/£18
1909	8,852,480		30p	£2	£6	£12/£18
1910	2,598,400		£2	£4	£8	£16/£25

All chemically darkened to avoid confusion with gold

FARTHINGS

Date	Mintage		Fine	V.F.	E.F.	abt. Unc/FDC
GEORGE V						
1911	5,196,800	★ 1a	25p	£1	£5	£9/£16
1911		★ 1b	50p	£2	£6	£12/£20
1912	7,669,760			50p	£2	£4/£8
1914	6,126,988	BRITT Obv.1	---	£1	£4	£8/£15
1914		BRIT T Obv.2	---	65p	£3	£6/£12
1915		BRITT	"Guesstimate"	£60	---	---/---
1915	7,129,254	BRIT T		£1	£5	£10/£20
1915	(noted 1998)			---	"Finest Unc."	£16/---
1916	10,993,325			50p	£3	£6/£12
1917	21,434,844			20p	£2	£4/£9
1918	19,362,818	left bright		15p	£2	£4/£8
1918	Rare, darkened finish			---	£6	£12/£20
1919	15,089,425			20p	£2	£5/£10
1920	11,480,536			20p	£3	£6/£12
1921	9,469,097			20p	£2	£5/£10
1922	9,956,983			20p	£1	£3/£6
1923	8,034,457			20p	£1	£3/£6
1924	8,733,414			25p	£1	£4/£8
1925	12,634,697			20p	£2	£4/£9
1926	9,792,397			20p	£1	£3/£6
1927	7,868,355			20p	£1	£3/£6
1928	11,625,600			15p	£1	£2/£4
1929	8,419,200			25p	£1	£3/£6
1930	4,195,200			25p	£1	£3/£6
1930	Bronze proof		(noted 2000)		"As struck"	£200
1931	6,595,200			25p	£1	£3/£6
1931	Bronze proof	(Peck 2347)	(noted 2000)		---	---/£165
1932	9,292,800		---	25p	£1	£3/£6
1932	Bronze proof	(noted 19990		"Superb FDC"		---/£175
1933	4,560,000		---	25p	£1	£3/£6
1933	Proof	(Peck 2353)	---	---	---	---/£195
1934	3,052,800		---	30p	£2	£5/£10
1934	Proof	(Peck 2355)	(noted 2001)		"Virt. as struck"	£200
1935	2,227,200		---	£1	£3	£6/£10
1936	9,734,400	posthumous issue		25p	£1	£3/£6
1936	Bronze proof	(noted 2000)		---	"FDC"	£300

"Fine"are sold. usually from The Tray 5p to 15p

The Modified Effigy was used from 1926 (see pages 37)

★ 1911 The 'standard' Peck obverse 1 has two variations:
Obverse 1a = above B.M. the neck is hollow.
Obverse 1b = above B.M. the neck is flat.

FARTHINGS abt.

Date	Mimntage	Dine	V.F.	E.F	Unc/FDC/FDC

EDWARD VIII Duke of Windsor

1937 Extremely rare · not issued for general circulation.   £12,000

GEORGE VI

BRONZE · 20mm

Date	Mintage	Dine	V.F.	E.F	Unc/FDC/FDC
1937	8,131,200	---	---	30p	60p/ £1/ £2
1937	26,402 proofs		---	---	£3/ £4/ £6
1938	7,449,600	---	20p	50p	£3/ £6/ £9
1939	31,440,000	---	---	15p	40p/80p/ £1
1940	18,360,000	---	---	25p	80p/ £2/ £3
1941	27,312,000	---	---	20p	60p/£1.5p/£2.5
1942	28,857,600	---	---	20p	60p/ £1/ £2
1943	33,345,600	---	---	20p	60p/£1.5p/£2.5
1944	25,137,600	---	---	15p	60p/ £1/ £2
1945	23,736,000	---	---	20p	50p/ £1/ £2
1946	23,364,800	---	---	15p	60p/ £1/ £2
1946	Bronze proof P2476 (possibly 3 only) (1999)				£230
1947	14,745,600	---	---	15p	60p/ £1/ £2
1948	16,622,400	---	---	15p	60p/ £1/ £2
1948	Bronze proof P2480 (1999) "abt FDC"				£180
1949	8,424,000	---	---	20p	75p/ £2/ £3
1949	Bronze proof (1994) "One of possibly 3 or 4"				£225
1950	10,324,800	---	---	15p	40p/80p/ £1
1950	17,513 proofs	---	---	---	£3/ £5/ £7
1951	14,016,000	---	---	---	40p/80p/ £1
1951	20,000 proofs	---	---	---	£3/ £5/ £7
1952	5,251,200	---	---	20p	60p/ £1/ £2
1952	Bronze proof P2488	---	---		---/£125/£175
1952	Bronze proof (1998) "Choice FDC, extremely rare"				£185

Proofs for all dates, those not listed are rarely seen; "guesstimate"   £250

ELIZABETH II

BRONZE · 20mm

Date	Mintage				Unc/FDC/FDC
1953	6,131,037 :				
1953	Obv.1 Rev. A	P2520	Currency Set		£1 /£1.50/ £2
1953	Obv.1 Rev. B	P2520A	---	£2	£8 /£16/£20
1953	Obv.2 Rev. A	P2520B	---	£3	£15/£25/£35
1953	Obv.2 Rev. B	P2521	---	10p	50p/ £1/£1.50
1953	40,000 proofs	P2522	(of P2521)		£3/ £5/ £7
1953	Proofs 2 + A	---	---	---	£40/£60/£80
1954	6,566,400	---	---	15p	30p/60p/ £1
1955	5,779,200	---	---	20p	40p/80p/ £2
1955	(noted 1999) "By/Buy the Bag"				

Colin Cooke offered 2,500 1955s "little beauties" £750

| 1955 | (noted 2000) | | | "500 little beauties" | £190 |
| 1956 | 1,996,800 | --- | --- | 50p | £1/£1.50/£3 |

Obverse 1 is poorly defined · the cross points TO a border bead.
Obverse 2 is sharper · the cross points BETWEEN two border beads.
Reverse A (dies of George VI) · 'F' points BETWEEN two beads.
Reverse B is similar but the 'F' points TO a border bead.

1953 Obverse/Reverse Rarity Scale   1 + A (C)   2 + A (ER)
                                      1 + B (R)   2 + B (VC)

(ER) = Extremely Rare · (R) = Rare · (C) = Common · (VC) = Very Common

Date	Mintage		Fine	V.F.	E.F.	abt. Unc/FDC.

GEORGE IV

LAUREATE HEAD · COPPER 28mm

Date	Mintage		Fine	V.F.	E.F.	abt. Unc/FDC.
1825	215,040		£10	£40	£100	£175/£225
1825	Proof		--	---	---	£150/£300
1826	9,031,630	Rev A	£6	£15	£45	£75/£95
1826	Proof	Rev A	--	--	---	----/£250
1826	Proof	Rev A bronzed			---	----/£180
1826		Rev B	£8	£20	£60	£120/£180
1826	Proof	Rev B	--	--	£75	£200/£300
1826	Proof	Rev B bronzed			---	----/£180
1827	5,376,000		£8	£20	£60	£90/£125

Rev A; Saltire of shield has two incuse lines P1433
Rev B; Saltire of shield has one raised line P1436
Saltire / St. Andrew's cross, often divided by line/s. (See page 17)

WILLIAM IV

BARE HEAD · COPPER 28mm

Date	Mintage	Fine	V.F.	E.F.	abt. Unc/FDC.
1831	806,400	£8	£20	£50	£95/£125
1831	Proofs, bronzed	head/tail reversed ↓			£200/----
1831	Proofs, bronzed	head/tail upright ↑			£300/----
1834	537,600	£8	£20	£50	£95/£125
1837	349,400 ·	£6	£15	£40	£80/£120

VICTORIA

YOUNG HEAD · DATE BELOW HEAD · COPPER 28mm

Date	Mintage	Fine	V.F.	E.F.	abt. Unc/FDC.
1838	456,960	£2	£5	£25	£60/£95
1839	Proofs, bronzed	---	---	---	£125/£250
1839	Proofs, bronzed, inverted reverse, from sets				£120/£225
1841	1,075,200	£2	£5	£20	£45/£75
1841	Broken die: DEI reads DF.I			£40	(2002)
1841	Ordinary issue, inverted reverse £25		£100	£225/£350
1841	Proofs, bronzed	---	---	---	£90/---
1841	Proof, in silver, on thick flan (2.8mm) "guesstimate"				£2000
1843	967,680	£18	£30	£75	£125/£175
1844	1,075,200	£3	£7	£30	£60/£85
1845	1,075,200	£35	£75	£250	£350/£475
1846	860,160	£4	£9	£40	£70/£95
1847	752,640	£4	£10	£45	£90/£135
1848	322,560	£10	£30	£90	£270/----
1848★	8 struck over 7	---	£7	£25	£50/£75
1848	8 struck over 3	---	£12	£30	---/---
1851	215,040 (no dots)	---	£6	£25	£50/£75
1851	Shield, 7 incuse dots	---	£12	£50	£100/£150
1852	637,056 (no dots)	---	£6	£25	£50/£75
1852	Shield, 7 incuse dots	---	£12	£50	£100/£150
1853	1,559,040	£2	£5	£10	£25/£45
1853	3 over 2	£9	£18	£40	£80/£120
1853	Proofs, bronzed, inverted reverse			---	£200/£300
1853	Copper proof	---	---	FDC	£175

VICTORIA

YOUNG HEAD · DATE BELOW HEAD · COPPER 28mm

Date	Mintage	Fine	V.F.	E.F.	abt. Unc/FDC.
1854	12,354,048 ?	£3	£6	£15	£25/£50
1855	1,455,837	£3	£6	£20	£60/£80
1856	1,942,080	£4	£9	£40	£80/£120
1857	1,182,720 (no dots)	---	£12	£50	£100/£150
1857	Shield, 7 incuse dots	---	£6	£25	£75/£125
1858	2,472,960	£2	£5	£20	£40/£75
1858	Smaller date	£2	£6	£30	£60/£90
1858	last 8 over 6	£4	£8	£25	£50/£75
1858	last 8 over 7	£3	£6	£20	£40/£65
1858	'Unrecorded' copper proof	---	---	£125/	----
1859	1,290,340	£8	£15	£45	£150/£200
1859	9 struck over 8	£6	£12	£40	£95/£130
1860**	Extremely rare	£200	£500	£2500	£4000

★ Variety more common than correctly dated piece
★★ Date is below head, not below Britannia

VICTORIA
"Bun" Head · DATE BELOW BRITANNIA · BRONZE 26mm

TYPE 1 · BEADED BORDERS:

1860	1 + A (P1750)	£1	£5	£20	£40/£50
1860	noted (Cooke 1999) "BU full lustre"	---			£48
1860	1 + A (P1751/52/53):				
	Proofs bronze and bronzed £450 to £650				
1860	A "mule" Type1/Type2	£1000		(Coincraft 1995)	

TYPE 2 · TOOTHED BORDERS:

Obv 2 has 7 berries. Obv 3 has 4 berries, all leaves have raised mid-ribs.
Obv 4 has 4 berries, but four leaves have double incuse lines to mid-ribs.
    Lighthouse :   B tapering, pointed   C cylindrical with rounded top.

1860	2 + B (P1754)	£1	£7	£25	£60/£75
1860	3 + B (P1756)	£1	£6	£25	£75/£100
1860	3 + C (P1757)	£1	£6	£25	£75/£100
1860	4 + B (P1758)	£4	£12	£30	£90/£120
1860★	F of HALF struck over P				
	"VF" $60 (£25 1987) (The Rawcliffe Halfpenny)				
1860	(noted 1997)	£25	£60	---	---/---
1861	54,118,400 Ten obv/rev combinations + proofs				
1861	Without signature	£1	£3	£15	£25/£40
1861	Signature on rock	£1	£4	£20	£50/£85
1861	3 + E but a proof thereof (2002)		"FDC"		£425

VICTORIA

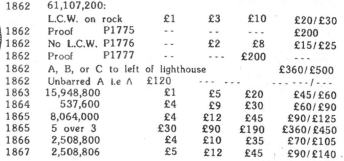

"Bun" Head · DATE BELOW BRITANNIA · BRONZE 26mm

Date	Mintage	Fine	V.F.	E.F.	abt. Unc/FDC.
1862	61,107,200:				
	L.C.W. on rock	£1	£3	£10	£20/£30
1862	Proof P1775	- -	- -	- - -	£200
1862	No L.C.W. P1776	- -	£2	£8	£15/£25
1862	Proof P1777	- -	- - -	£200	- - -
1862	A, B, or C to left of lighthouse				£360/£500
1862	Unbarred A i.e ∧	£120	- - - - - -		- - - - - -/- - -
1863	15,948,800	£1	£5	£20	£45/£60
1864	537,600	£4	£9	£30	£60/£90
1865	8,064,000	£4	£12	£45	£90/£125
1865	5 over 3	£30	£90	£190	£360/£450
1866	2,508,800	£4	£10	£35	£70/£105
1867	2,508,806	£5	£12	£45	£90/£140

★ FARTHINGS of this date bear Fs with little or no lower serif to the lower horizontal bar (illustr.) Perhaps the first halfpennies were struck with the same, or a similar, type-face and were overstruck to avoid having HALP PENNYs as well as PARTHINGS.

"POINTINGS" are very much the key to some varieties. A principal feature such as a letter or ornament is selected and its 'attitude' is used to indicate the use of a different die-punch. Thus HALFPENNY indicates that the upright of the 'L' is *pointing* to a rim bead. HALFPENNY that 'L' points between two beads. Many dies are used to complete a full year's striking. New dies are usually identical being from the same, original punch. Differences are, therefore, interesting nusmismatically and unequal strikings must, eventually, show up in valuations.

HALFPENNIES

BRONZE 26mm

VICTORIA

"Bun" Head · DATE BELOW BRITANNIA

Date	Mintage	Fine		V.F.	E.F.	abt. Unc/FDC.
1868	3,046,400		£4	£10	£40	£80/£120
1868	Cupro-nickel proof			(noted 1993)		"FDC" £325
1869	3,225,600		£5	£25	£75	£150/£225
1870	4,350,739		£4	£9	£30	£60/£90
1871	1,075,280 ?		£15	£45	£145	£300/£450
1872	4,659,410		£1	£4	£24	£36/£55
1873	3,404,880		£2	£10	£35	£75/£100
1874	1,347,665		£4	£20	£65	£200/£250
1874	Portrait as 1874H		£1	£4	£24	£35/£55
1874H	5,017,600		£1	£5	£25	£50/£70
1874H	Proof			(noted 1993)		"FDC" £150
1875	5,430,815		£1	£2	£20	£60/£90
1875H	1,254,400		£3	£6	£30	£60/£80
1876H	6,809,600		£1	£4	£25	£45/£65
1877	5,209,505		£1	£2	£16	£35/£55
1878	1,425,535		£3	£12	£36	£150/£256
1879	3,582,545		£1	£5	£20	£40/£60
1880	2,423,465		£2	£5	£20	£40/£60
1881	2,007,515		£2	£5	£20	£40/£60
1881H	1,792,000		£1	£3	£15	£40/£60
1882H	4,480,000		£1	£3	£15	£30/£50
1883	Portrait as 1874 to 1882H		---	£15	£45	£90/---
1883	3,000,725		£3	£6	£25	£50/£75
1884	6,989,580		£1	£2	£12	£25/£40
1885	8,600,574		£1	£2	£12	£25/£40
1886	8,586,155		£1	£2	£10	£25/£40
1887	10,701,305		£1	£2	£9	£25/£40
1888	6,814,070		£1	£3	£12	£25/£40
1889	7,748,234		£1	£2	£12	£30/£50
1889	9 over 8		£8	£30	£90	£180/£260
1890	11,254,235		£1	£2	£10	£25/£45
1891	13,192,260		£1	£2	£10	£25/£40
1892	2,478,335		£2	£3	£10	£25/£45
1893	7,229,344		£1	£2	£9	£25/£45
1894	1,767,635		£1	£3	£10	£35/£55

Old, or Widow Head

BRONZE 26mm

1895	3,032,154	P1950	£1	£3	£6	£15/£30
1896	9,142,500	P1951	£1	£2	£5	£10/£25
1897	8,690,315	P1951A	£1	£2	£6	£12/£25
1897	Horizon higher	P1952	£2	£4	£7	£12/£20
1898	8,595,180	P1953	£1	£3	£6	£15/£20
1899	12,108,001	P1954	£1	£3	£7	£15/£25
1900	13,805,190	P1955	£1	£2	£6	£12/£16
1901	11,127,360	P1956	£1	£2	£4	£9/£12

Date	Mintage	Fine	V.F.	E.F.	abt. Unc/FDC
EDWARD VII					
1902	13,672,960	---	£2	£5	£10/£15
1902	LOW TIDE variety	£2	£15	£34	£60/£90
1903	11,450,880	---	£2	£9	£16/£25
1904	8,131,200	£3	£6	£15	£30/£40
1905	10,124,800	---	£1	£5	£22/£30
1906	11,101,440	---	£1	£4	£12/£20
1907	16,849,280	---	£1	£4	£12/£25
1908	16,620,800	---	£1	£5	£20/£28
1909	8,279,040	---	£4	£12	£20/£30
1910	10,769,920	---	£1	£8	£15/£20

Proofs exist for 1902; they are very rare.

"LOW TIDE" VARIETY referred to above and on page 24 may be determined thus: if the horizon meets Britannia at the point, below the knee, where right and left legs cross; NORMAL tide is indicated. If, however, the horizon meets Britannia at a much lower point - nearer the hem of her drape - then a LOW TIDE variety has been detected.

GEORGE V   BRITANNIA REVERSE · BRONZE 26mm

Date	Mintage		Fine	V.F.	E.F.	abt. Unc/FDC
1911	12,570,880	★Obv. 1a		£2	£4	£10/£15
1911	★Obverse 1b		---	£3	£6	£12/£20
1912	21,185,920	.	---	£2	£4	£15/£25
1913	17,476,480		---	£2	£5	£20/£30
1914	20,289,111		---	£2	£4	£12/£20
1915	21,563,040		---	£3	£6	£15/£25
1916	39,386,143		---	£1	£4	£12/£20
1917	38,245,436		---	£1	£4	£15/£25
1918	22,321,072		---	£1	£4	£15/£25
1919	28,104,001		---	£1	£4	£15/£25
1920	35,146,793		---	£1	£3	£12/£20
1920	Trial in nickel (noted 1998) "Superb Mint State"					£375
1921	28,027,293		---	£1	£3	£10/£15
1922	10,734,964		---	£2	£5	£12/£20
1923	12,266,282		---	£1	£4	£12/£20
1924	13,971,038		---	£1	£4	£12/£20
1925	12,216,123	Head as for 1924		£1	£5	£15/£25
1925	Modified Head	as for 1926		£3	£8	£12/£20

1911   ★ Obverse 1a has a hollow neck · Obverse 1b has a flat neck
1911/12   Some dies were punched with date close to line of exergue
Small gap = Rev A   Clear gap = Rev B
Combinations: 1a + A · 1a + B   1b + A · 1b + B
1925/27   Effigy modified to aid striking of all coins
1928   Smaller head adopted for halfpennies and pennies

16   HALFPENNIES   BRONZE 26mm

Date	Mintage	Fine	V.F.	E.F.	abt. Unc/FDC
GEORGE V		BRITANNIA REVERSE			
1926	6,712,306	---	£2	£6	£10/£15
1927	15,589,622	---	£1	£4	£10/£15
1928	20,935,200	SMALLER HEAD:	£1	£2	£6/£12
1928	Proof	---	(noted 1988)		---/£175
1929	25,680,000	---	£1	£5	£10/£15
1930	12,532,800	---	£1	£2	£6/£12
1931	16,137,600	---	£1	£2	£6/£9
1932	14,448,000	---	£1	£2	£5/£8
1933	10,560,000	---	£1	£2	£5/£8
1934	7,704,000	---	£1	£5	£10/£15
1935	12,180,000	---	£1	£2	£5/£9
1935	(noted 1995) (P2321) Bronze proof		"F.D.C."		£150
1936	23,008,800	---	£1	£2	£4/£6

Proofs 1926 to 1936 inclusive: British Museum.

EDWARD VIII   *(Duke of Windsor)*   GOLDEN HIND
1937	Excessively rare	"Guesstimate"	£10,000/£15,000

GEORGE VI   Reverse GOLDEN HIND · BRONZE 25mm

Date	Mintage	Fine	V.F.	E.F.	abt. Unc/FDC
1937	24,504,000	---	---	50p	£1/£3
1937	26,402 proofs		---	---	£3/£5
1938	40,320,000	---	10p	£1	£2/£4
1939	28,924,800	---	10p	£1	£3/£5
1940	32,162,400	---	30p	£2	£4/£6
1940	Thinner rim, shorter teeth	Freeman 435			£5/£10
1941	45,120,000	---	5p	50p	£1/£3
1942	17,908,800	---	5p	50p	£1/£3
1943	76,200,000	---	10p	50p	£1/£3
1944	81,840,000	---	5p	£1	£2/£4
1945	57,000,000	---	5p	£1	£2/£4
1946	22,725,600	---	30p	£2	£4/£6
1947	21,266,400	---	10p	£1	£2/£4
1948	26,947,200	---	10p	50p	£1/£2
1949	24,744,000	---	10p	£1	£4/£6
1950	24,153,600	---	10p	£2	£6/£9
1950	17,513 proofs		---	FDC	£9
1951	14,868,000	---	20p	£2	£4/£6
1951	20,000 proofs		---	FDC	£5
1952	33,278,400	---	10p	50p	£2/£4

Proofs of all dates. Those not listed above · £150/£175

```
        1940
  * * * *
   L    P      = Rev A

  * * * *
   L    P      = Rev B

  *
   L           = Rev C

  See 'pointings'
    page 13
```

1949	IND:IMP (Emperor of India) discontinued · all coins
1954	BRITT:OMN discontinued · all coins
1969	Halfpenny demonetized · 1st August

ELIZABETH II

Date	Mintage	Fine	V.F.	E.F.	abt. Unc/FDC/FDC
1953	8,910,000 :				
1953	Obverse 1	---	---	---	£3/£5
1953	Obverse 2	---	10p	20p	£1/£2
1953	40,000 proofs		---	---	£3/£6
1954	19,375,200	---	10p	£1	£2/£3/£4
1955	18,465,600	---	10p	£1	£2/£3/£4
1956	21,799,200	---	---	£1	£2/£3/£4
1957	39,672,000	---	---	20p	£1/£2/£3
1957	Variety has a calm sea		£1	£2	£4/£8/£12
1958	66,331,200	---	---	---	50p/£1/£2
1958	Proof (noted 1999)		---	---	---/£150
1959	79,176,000	---	---	---	50p/£1/£2
1960	41,340,000	---	---	---	50p/£1/£2
1961	Decimal Patterns see page XXX			---	---
1962	41,779,200	---	---	---	15p/50p/£2
1963	42,720,000	---	---	---	15p/40p/£2
1964	78,583,200	---	---	---	15p/30p/£1
1965	98,083,200	---	---	---	15p/30p/£1
1965	Proofs struck in gold		---	---	£1,250
1965	Error New Zealand reverse			---	£450
1966	95,289,600 ·	---	---	---	5p/15p/30p
1966	Struck in nickel-brass		---	---	£350
1966	Struck in aluminium		---	---	£250
1967	146,490,400 Narrow rim			---	5p/15p/50p
1967	(KB Coins '94) Wide rim "BU"				£2.50

Total for 1967 includes 46,226,400 struck in 1968

| 1970 | 750,424 LAST STERLING: | | | | |

Proofs (1971/75)   £1/£2/£3

Proofs of all dates. Those not listed above · £125/£145

Cross points BETWEEN rim beads	★ ★ +	= Obverse 1
Cross points TO a rim bead	★ ★ ★ +	= Obverse 2

THIS PANEL REFERS TO PENNIES ON NEXT PAGE

Saltire/St. Andrew's Cross varieties :

A · No central line along arms of saltire

B · Thin raised line along saltire

C · Thick/broad raised line

PENNIES
DATE BELOW HEAD · COPPER 34mm

GEORGE IV

Date	Mintage	Rev.	Peck No.	Fine	V.F.	E.F.	abt. Unc/FDC
1825	1,075,200	A	P1420	£12	£25	£75	£200/£250
1825	Proofs	A	P1421	---	---	---	£200/£300
1826	5,913,000	A	P1422	£8	£25	£80	£200/£250
1826	Bronsed proof	A	P1423	---	---	---	£150/£200
1826	Copper proof	A	P1424	---	---	---	£150/£200
1826	Currency	B	P1425	£12	£25	£75	£125/£170
1826	Bronzed proof	B	P1426	---	---	---	£150/£200
1826	Currency	C	P1427	£15	£30	£120	£200/£300
1826	Bronzed proof	C	P1428	---	---	---	£200/£275
1826	Copper proof	C	P1429	---	---	---	£300/£450
1827	1,451,520	A	P1430				
1827	A Ext. rare	Fair £20		£100	£250	£1250	£2500/£4000
1827	A (noted 1991)			"no corrosion"	"gd.VF"	£290	-----/-----

WILLIAM IV

Date	Mintage		Peck No.	Fine	V.F.	E.F.	abt. Unc/FDC
1831	806,400 no WW		P1455	£12	£45	£100	£350/£425
1831	(noted 1999)				"superb EF"	£110	----/----
1831	Bronzed proofs			---	---	---	£200/£250
1831	.W.W Incuse initials on truncation				£60	£175	£400/£500
1831	W.W Incuse Initials		P1458*	£20	£80	£225	£450/£600
1834	322,560		P1459	£15	£50	£130	£260/£400
1837	174,720		P1460	£40	£95	£225	£500/£600

VICTORIA
Young Head · DATE BELOW HEAD 34mm

Date	Mintage		Peck No.	Fine	V.F.	E.F.	abt. Unc/FDC
1839	Bronzed proof DEF : o.t.		1479			£150	£300/£450
1841	913,920	REG:	1480	£5	£10	£30	£60/£90
1841	Proofs			---	---	---	£250/£400
1841	Proof in silver	(1980 "As Struck")					£1,500
1841	No colon	REG	1484	£5	£10	£30	£60/£90
1841	No colon	(noted 2001)		"gdE.F."		£40	---/---
1843	483,830	REG:	1486	£25	£95	£350	£700/----
1843	No colon	REG	1485	£30	£100	£400	£800/----
1844	215,040		1487	£8	£12	£40	£80/£120
1845	322,560		1489	£9	£20	£75	£150/£225
1846	483,840	DEF :	1490	£8	£15	£50	£100/£150
1846		DEF:	1491	£8	£16	£65	£125/£175
1847	430,080	DEF:	1492	£5	£12	£45	£95/£130
1847		DEF :	1493	£5	£12	£45	£95/£130
1848	161,280		1496	£3	£10	£45	£95/£130
1848	8 over 6		1494	--	£25	£75	£150/£225
1848	8 over 7		1495	--	£12	£40	£80/£120
1849	268,800		1497	£40	£125	£500	£1000/£1500
1851	432,224	DEF :	1498	£6	£15	£50	£90/£125
1851		DEF:	1499	£8	£20	£60	£120/£165

VICTORIA

Date	Mintage	Peck	Fine	V.F.	E.F.	Unc/abtFDC
				Young Head · DATE BELOW HEAD 34mm		
1853	1,021,440 DEF :	1500	£4	£9	£25	£50/£80
1853	Narrow date		---	---	£12	£20/£40
1853	Proofs - copper and bronzed			---	---	£250/£500
1853	(noted 2001)			Bronzed proof	"nr.FDC".	£250
1853	DEF:	1503	£3	£8	£30	£75/£110
1853	Plain trident	1504	£3	£12	£30	£60/£90
1854	4 over 3	1505	£15	£45	£95	£135/£225
1854	6,720,000 p.t.	1506	£1	£6	£20	£40/£85
1854	Ornam trident	1507	£1	£6	£20	£40/£80
1854	(noted 1999)			"FDC full lustre exceptional"		£95
1855	5,273,866 o.t.	1508	£1	£7	£20	£40/£65
1855	Plain trident	1509	£1	£6	£20	£40/£60
1856	1,212,288 DEF:	p.t.	£12	£42	£150	£300/£400
1856	Plain trident proof		---	---	---	£250/£500
1856	DEF :	o.t.	£7	£35	£95	£250/£350
1857	752,640 DEF:	p.t.	£2	£6	£25	£50/£75
1857	DEF :	o.t.	£3	£8	£30	£60/£90
1857	Smaller date	p.t.	£2	£6	£25	£50/£75
1858	1,559,040:					
	8 over 3	1515	--	£22	£60	£120/---
	8 over 6		--	---	£60	---
	8 over 7	1516	--	£6	£25	£50/£75
	Smaller date	1517	£1	£6	£25	£50/£75
	Large date no W.W.	1518	£1	£5	£20	£40/£60
1859	1,075,200 Large date		£3	£8	£30	£60/£90
1859	9 over 8		£4	£16	£42	£95/£130
1859	Smaller date		£3	£9	£35	£80/£125
1859	Proof		---	---	---	£500/£750
1860	60 struck over 59		£150	£400	£950	----/---
1860	60 struck over 59		↓Rev.	£500	£950	----/£1500

DEF: = near colon - DEF : = far colon - o.t. = ornamental trident
plain tridents have near colons   p.t. = plain trident
All have ornamental tridents from 1839 to 1851

NEAR COLON:

FAR COLON :

PENNIES
VICTORIA · "Bun" Head
BRONZE · DATE BELOW BRITANNIA · 31mm

1860 5,053,440 TYPE 1

BEADED RIM BORDER
Obverse: L.C.WYON ON TRUNCATION

Rev	Peck		Fine.	V.F.	E.F.	Abt. Unc.
A	1617		£3	£15	£35	£80
B	1619		£6	£30	£70	£160
B	1620	extra heavy flan		---	£750	---
B	1620A	proof in gold (noted 1997)			---	£15,000
B	1621	silver proof	--	---	---	(£500 EF+)
B	1622	bronzed proof	--	---	---	£500
C	1623		£10	£45	£95	---
Mule	1624	bead obv/tooth rev		£95	£250	£500
Mule	1628	tooth obv/bead rev		£250	£600	£1200

TYPE 2 **TOOTHED RIM/BORDER**

Obverse: L.C.WYON ON or BELOW TRUNCATION

Rev	Peck		Fine.	V.F.	E.F.	Abt. Unc.
C★	1625	signature on	---	£9	£35	£70
C★		(S & B 1995) "gdEF much lustre"			£45	---
D	1626	signature on	.---	£25	£95	£225
C★	1629	signature on	---	---	£35	£70
C★	1630	struck on heavy flan	---	---	£250	---
C★	1631	bronze proof	---	---	---	£250
C★	1632	signature below	---	£10	£40	£75
C★	1633	no sig. 15 leaves	---	£50	£90	---
C★	1635	no sig. 16 leaves	---	£50	£90	---
	1634	ONF PENNY variety: damaged die	£12	£45	£175	£375/ ---
	2051	Wyon Pattern MDCCCLX · nickel alloy : (Seaby 1989) "gdEF"			£450	---- / ----

The design is described, in exquisite detail, by Michael J. Freeman in his book "The Bronze Coinage of Great Britain".

1860 reverse: L.C.W. incuse below shield

Rev. A = crosses outlined with treble incuse lines, Britannia's thumb touches cross of St. George, no rock to left of lighthouse.

Peck/ Freeman equiv.
Peck 'A' = Fr/man 'B'
Peck 'B' = Fr/man 'A'
Peck 'C' = Fr/man 'C'
Peck 'C★'= Fr/man 'D'
Peck 'D' = Fr/man 'E'

Rev. B = crosses outlined by close, double, raised lines, Britannia's thumb does not touch cross no rock to left of lighthouse.

Rev. C = similar to Rev. B, but lines thinner and wider apart, small rock to left of lighthouse.

Rev. C★ = as Rev. C, but with minor modifications to rocks and sea and, of course,
a toothed border.

Rev. D = as Rev. C, but L.C.W. incuse below foot.

VICTORIA "Bun" Head DATE BELOW BRITANNIA - 31mm abt.

Rev	Peck			F.	V.F.	E.F.	UNC/FDC

1861 36,449,280 Obverse: L.C.WYON ON or BELOW TRUNCATION

Rev	Peck			F.	V.F.	E.F.	UNC/FDC
C★	1637	signature on		- - -	£120	- - -	- - -
F	1638	no signature		£20	£75	- - -	- - -
C★	1639	sig. below		£5	£12	£30	£60/£80
F	1642	no signature		£20	£75	- - -	- - -
C★	1643	no sig 15 leaves	£35	- - -	- - -	- - -	
C★	1644	no sig 16 leaves	£5	£12	£30	£60/£80	
		6 over 8 Fair £50	£95	£225	- - -	- - -	
F	1646	no sig		£5	£12	£30	£60/£80

OBVERSE 5 · No Signature · Wreath of 16 leaves · Raised midribs
REVERSE F · No signature · Thumb does not touch St.George's cross

Date	Mintage				
1862	50,534,400	£1	£9	£25	£40/£60
1862	Bronzed proof	- - -	- - -	- - -	£400
1862		Date from halfpenny die (smaller):			
	Fair £60 £95 £250	- - -			- - - -
1862	8 over 6	"gdVF"	£275		(Seaby 1989)
1862	Pattern cu-nickel P2060			"FDC"	£600
1863	28,062,720 (P1655)	£1	£10	£40	£80/£100
1863	Bronzed proof	- - -	- - -	- - -	£250
1863	Die number below date:				
	2 below	£300	- - -		(noted 1996)
	3 below Fair £100	- - -	- - -		(noted 1988)
	4 below	£250	- - -		(noted 1998)
1864	3,440,646 Plain 4	£15	£50	£200	£350/£450
1864	Crosslet 4	£20	£75	£250	£425/£525
1865	8,601,600	£2	£9	£45	£90/- - - -
1865	5 over 3	£30	£75	£175	£400/£750
1865	Pattern P2061	- - -	- - -	"nrFDC"	£300
1866	9,999,360	£3	£10	£60	£120/- - - -
1867	5,483,520	£4	£15	£40	£90/- - - -
1867	Proof in silver (noted 2000)	- - -		"abt.FDC"	£667
1868	1,182,720	£6	£20	£75	£150/- - - -
1868	Bronze proof P1681		(noted 1998)		£425
1868	Copper-nickel proof	- -	- - -	£250	£400
1869	2,580,480	£30	£95	£450	£650/- - - -
1870	5,695,022	£5	£15	£75	£200/£300
1871	1,290,318	£15	£60	£200	£400/£500
1872	8,494,572	£3	£12	£30	£75/- - - -
1873	8,494,200	£3	£12	£30	£60/£80

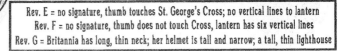

Rev. E = no signature, thumb touches St. George's Cross; no vertical lines to lantern
Rev. F = no signature, thumb does not touch Cross, lantern has six vertical lines
Rev. G = Britannia has long, thin neck; her helmet is tall and narrow; a tall, thin lighthouse

PENNIES
VICTORIA · "Bun" Head
DATE BELOW BRITANNIA - 31mm

O/R	Peck	F.	V.F.	E.F.	. abt. UNC/FDC

OBVERSE 5; and OBVERSE 6 (a MORE MATRONLY PORTRAIT)
REVERSE F; and REVERSE G (a LESS GRACEFUL BRITANNIA)

1874   5,621,86 :

O/R	Peck	F.	V.F.	E.F.	abt. UNC/FDC
5/F	1690	£5	£15	£50	£100/£150
5/G	1691	£10	£30	£60	----/----
6/F	1692	£5	£15	£50	£100/£150
6/G	1693	£10	£30	£60	----/----

1874H   6,666,240 :

'H' centrally, in exergue, below date indicates coins struck at Heaton Mint

		F.	V.F.	E.F.	abt. UNC/FDC
5/F	1694	£5	£15	£50	£100/£175
5/G	1695	£10	£25	£60	---/----
6/F	1696	£5	£15	£50	£90/----
6/G	1697	£5	£15	£50	£85/----
6/G	1698 Bronze proof	--	-----		£350
1875	10,691,040	£2	£7	£25	£50/£75
1875H	752,640	£25	£80	£200	£400/----
1875H	(at auction 2002) "E.F. with some lustre" £897				----
1875H	Proof P1706	(noted 2001) "FDC"			£500
1876H	11,074,560	£3	£9	£45	£75/---
1877	Narrow date	£200	---	---	---/---
1877	9,624,747	£2	£7	£45	£80/£125
1877	Proof cupro-nickel	---	"nr.FDC"		---/£700
1878	2,764,470	£3	£10	£40	£80/£120
1878	Proof P1713	---	"nr.FDC"		---/£275
1879	7,666,476	£2	£6	£24	£60/£95
1879	Narrow date	£10	£20	£60	£120/---
1879	Re-touched Obv. P1715			£75	"gdEF"
1880	3,000,831	£3	£10	£40	£80/£120
1880	Proof (noted 1999)			"abt.FDC"	---/£500
1881	2,302,261	£2	£10	£42	£65/£95
1881	Portrait 'aged' further:				
	P1722	£4	£15	£50	£75/£95
1881H	3,763,200	£2	£10	£25	£50/£75
1881H	(noted 2001) "Unc good lustre"				£70
1881H	Heraldically coloured shield				£50/---

VICTORIA "Bun" Head (continued)

Date	Mintage	F.	V.F.	E.F.	Abt. Unc/FDC
1882H	7,526,400	£2	£6	£20	£40/£60
1882	No H (beware removal)			£600	£900/----
1883	6,237,438	£2	£7	£25	£45/£70
1884	11,702,802	£2	£5	£20	£40/£60
1885	7,145,862	£2	£5	£20	£35/£55
1886	6,087,759	£2	£4	£15	£30/£45
1887	5,315,085	£1	£4	£15	£30/£45
1887	Aluminium pattern (P2175)			(1999)	£400
1888	5,125,020	£1	£4	£15	£30/£45
1889	12,559,737	£1	£4	£14	£26/£40
1889	Narrow date (P1745)			£25	---/---
1890	15,330,840	£1	£4	£15	£30/£45
1891	17,885,961	£1	£4	£15	£35/£50
1892	10,501,671	£1	£4	£15	£30/£45
1893	8,161,737	£1	£5	£16	£32/£48
1894	3,883,452	£3	£12	£30	£60/£80

Proofs for 1881, 1884/85/86 and 1890/91/92
All proofs except, perhaps, 1888 £400/£500

VICTORIA Old, Veiled, or Widow Head

1895	5,395,830 ·	Rev B	£4	£8	£18/£30
1895	No sea Rev A	£10	£30	£80	£175/£250
1895	Pattern (P2066)	(noted 1999)			---/£800
1896	24,147,156	£1	£3	£8	£16/£30
1896	9 and 6 further apart		£5	£10	£25/£40
1897	20,756,620	£1	£3	£6	£12/£20
1897	Higher horizon		---	£100	£200
1898	14,296,836	£1	£3	£10	£20/£30
1899	26,441,069	£1	£4	£8	£18/£36
1900	31,778,109	---	£1	£4	£8/£16
1900	Proofs	---	---	"FDC"	£300
1901	22,205,568	---	£1	£5	£10/£15
1901	Proofs	---	---	"FDC"	£300

1895	Rev A, trident to P is 2mm; no sea behind
1895	Rev B, trident to P is 1mm; sea behind (to left of) Britannia

24 PENNIES

Date	Mintage	Fine	V.F.	E.F.	abt. Unc/FDC
EDWARD VII					BRONZE 31mm
1902	26,976,768	30p	£3	£5	£12/£20
1902	LOW TIDE variety	£3	£10	£25	£40/£60
1903	21,415,296	---	£4	£10	£20/£30
1903	Open '3'	£15	£25	£60	---/---
1904	12,913,152	---	£5	£15	£25/£35
1905	17,783,808	---	£4	£12	£20/£30
1906	37,989,504	---	£4	£8	£15/£25
1907	47,322,240	---	£3	£9	£18/£24
1908	31,506,048	---	£3	£10	£20/£30
1908	(Coincraft 1998) lists a matt proof on thick flan				£1,000
1909	19,617,024	---	£3	£9	£18/£24
1910	29,549,184	---	£4	£10	£20/£30
GEORGE V					BRONZE 31mm
1911	23,079,168	(1 + A)	£4		£8	£15/£22
1911	Hollow neck	(see page 6)		(1988 GEF £20)	
1912	48,306,048	(1 + A)	£3	£8	£15/£22
1912H	16,800,000	(1 + A)	£5	£20	£30/£45
1913	65,497,872	(2 + B)	£3	£10	£20/£30
1914	50,820,997	---	£3	£8	£15/£25
1915	47,310,807	---	£3	£5	£15/£25
1916	86,411,165	---	£2	£3	£9/£12
1917	107,905,436	---	£2	£3	£10/£15
1918	84,227,372	---	£2	£3	£12/£20
1918H	3,660,800	£1	£10	£70	£140/£200
1918H	(noted 1999) "BU full lustre"				£165/----
1918KN	Inc above	£2	£15	£95	£200/£260
1919	113,761,090	---	£1	£5	£10/£15
1919H	5,209,600	£1	£10	£70	£140/£200
1919KN	Inc above	£2	£20	£100	£250/£300
1920	124,693,485	(2 + B)	£2	£5	£10/£20
1920	(P2259)	(3 + B)	---	---	---/---
1921	129,717,693	(2 + B)	£2	£5	£12/£22
1921	(P2261)	(3 + B)	£2	£9	£22/£30
1922	16,346,711	(3 + B)	£3	£15	£30/£50
1923 to 1925	None	---	---	---	
1926	4,498,519	---	£5	£25	£50/£75
1926	Modified effigy	£7	£20	£200	£450/£650
1927	60,989,561	---	£2	£4	£6/£10

(vertical note): 188 has B whilst B has 163 teeth has A rev of circle Toothed

1913 1+A rarer than 2+B; rarer still are 2+A and 1+B

SMALLER HEAD

Date	Mintage	Fine	V.F.	E.F.	abt. Unc/FDC
1928	50,178,000	---	£2	£4	£8/£12
1929	49,132,800	---	£1	£5	£7/£12
1930	29,097,600	---	£1	£6	£9/£15
1931	19,843,200	---	£1	£7	£14/£21
1932	8,277,600	---	£3	£15	£30/£45
1932	Proof (P2278) (noted 1999)		"FDC"		£300
1933	7 or 8 plus "patterns" (Spink 1994)				£25,300
1933	Pattern by Lavrillier		(1986)		£4,100
1933	A uniface	---	(1980 £28,750)		£50,000
1934	13,965,600	---	£2	£9	£20/£30
1935	56,070,000	---	£1	£3	£4/£8
1935	Bronze proof (noted 1999)		"FDC"		£250
1936	154,296,000	---	£1	£2	£3/£6

Proofs for all dates from 1926 to 1936 except 1933

H-Heaton Mint Mark

KN-Kings Norton Mint Mark

Obv. 1: colon close to 'A' GRA: BRITT

Obv. 2: stops midway cramped; GRA:BRITT

Obv. 3: as obv. 2 but words farther apart; GRA : BRITT

In addition to the 7, possibly 8, pennies listed at left (left-hand pair above); there were patterns, possibly four, struck from dies engraved by André Lavrillier (right-hand pair above) having a 'military' King George V, a thick trident and a sea of wavy lines. Yet another 1933 penny is uni-face: having a "tail" but the "head" replaced by the word MODEL. The 1933 set from St. Mary's Church, Hawksworth Wood, was offered for sale at Sotheby's in 1972. It fetched £7,000. This set was one of those placed under foundation stones laid by King George in 1933.

Date	Mintage		Fine	V.F.	E.F.	abt. Unc/FDC

EDWARD VIII (Duke of Windsor)
1937   Specimen.strikings only,"guesstimate" from £15,000

GEORGE VI   BRONZE 31mm

Date	Mintage		Fine	V.F.	E.F.	abt. Unc/FDC
1937	88,896,000		---	50p	£1	£2/£4
1937	26,402	proofs		---	£3	£4/£8
1938	121,560,000		---	20p	£1	£2/£4
1939	55,560,000		---	60p	£2	£4/£6
1940	42,284,400		£1	£3	£6	£10/£20
1941 to	1943 none		---	---	---	---
1944	42,600,000		---	60p	£3	£6/£9
1944	not toned by	Royal Mint		---	---	£8/£16
1945	79,531,200		---	50p	£2	£4/£6
1945	Doubled 9		£1	£5	£25	---
1946	66,855,600		---	30p	£2	£4/£6
1947	52,220,400		---	30p	£2	£3/£4
1948	63,961,200		---	10p	£1	£2/£3
1949	14,324,400		---	20p	£1	£2/£4
1950	240,000		£2	£6	£12	£18/£25
1950	17,513	proofs		---	FDC	£20
1951	120,000		£3	£8	£12	£20/£30
1951	20,000	proofs		---	FDC	£18

Proofs for all dates. Those not listed above, £250

			●●●●
1937	Rev Aa	Ns point to border teeth	N N ●●●●
1937	Rev Ab	Ns point between teeth (b is rarer)	N N
1940	Rev Ab	has single exergue line	
1940	Rev B	has double exergue line (Ab is rarer)	
1944	Rev Ba	waves touch exergue	
1944	Rev Bb	gap between waves and exergue	

Date	Mintage	V.F.	E.F.	abt. Unc/FDC
1953	Pattern (not in Peck) unique ? : has toothed (not beaded) border		Spink	£1,950
1953	1,308,400 (from the 'Plastic' Set)	£1		£2/£4
1953	(noted 1999)	"BU. Full lustre"		£5
1953	40,000 proofs	. - - -		£6/£9
1953	Pattern from sand-blasted dies	- - -	- - -	£250
1954	1 retrieved from change.		Now in British Museum.	
1954	It is believed there are others	"guesstimate"		£24,000
1955	to 1960 none	- - -	- - -	- - -
1961	48,313,400	- - -	- - -	25p/60p
1962	157,588,600	- - -	- - -	20p/50p
1963	119,733,600 .	- - -	- - -	- - -/25p
1964	153,294,000	- - -	- - -	12p/25p
1965	121,310,400	- - -	- - -	15p/50p
1965	In gold, unofficial, (Christies 1989 £1300)			£2500
1966	165,739,200	- - -	- - -	- - -/25p
1966	2 (so far) Jersey penny obverse.	(Auction 1992)		£605
1967	155,280,000	- - -	- - -	- - -/15p
1968	170,400,000 all dated 1967			
1969	219,360,000 all dated 1967			
1970	109,524,000 all dated 1967:	654,564,000		
	Proofs for some dates. 1970 proofs from the sets	£2		£3/£4

NOTE ON BULLION VALUE. Although the collector's value of a worn coin is listed as face-value only (---), a silver one may have a higher, bullion value because of the precious metal in it. At one time pre 1947 silver coins were worth 4 times face value and pre 1920 ones up to 7 or 8 times. Buyers now make quotations on a day-to-day basis. A large enough quantity to sell is necessary to offset the cost of mailing. Check rates on Teletext. Be sure to contact the dealer before sending. Offers in 2002 averaged £4 per £1 face value pre-1947 and £8 per £1 face-value for pre-1920.

THREE HALFPENCES   FOR COLONIAL USE

Date	Mintage	Fine	V.F.	E.F.	abt. Unc/FDC
WILLIAM IV					SILVER 12mm
1834	800,448	£5	£10	£30	£50/£60
1835	633,600	£10	£20	£50	£90/£120
1835	5 struck over 4	£6	£12	£30	£55/£75
1836	158,400	£3	£12	£25	£40/£60
1837	30,624	£10	£25	£90	£150/£180
VICTORIA					SILVER 12mm
.1838	538,560	£3	£9	£20	£30/£45
1839	760,320	£2	£8	£18	£25/£40
1840	95,040	£7	£20	£50	£90/£125
1841	158,400	£4	£10	£25	£50/£65
1842	1,869,120	£4	£10	£25	£50/£65
1843	475,200	£1	£4	£12	£25/£40
1843	43 over 34	£5	£18	£40	£60/£90
1843	43 over 34	Proof	- - -	- - -	£500
1860	160,000 ·	£2	£10	£35	£65/£95
1862	256,000	£2	£10	£30	£60/£90
1862	Proof	(Seaby 1990)	abt.FDC		£475
1870	Proof, or pattern	(1986)	- - -		£325
1870	Proof, or pattern	(1996)	- - -		£750
1870	Proof, or pattern	(1999)	- - -		£950
1870	Proof, or pattern	(2000)	- - -		£950

GEORGE IV

SILVER 16mm

Date	Mintage	Fine	V.F.	E.F.	Unc	abt. FDC
1822	small head (from Maundy 2d)	£3	£12	£25	£40/£50	
1822	from Maundy proof set	- - -	- - -	- - -	- - -/- - -	
1823	larger 'normal' head	£1	£6	£12	£24/£36	
1824		£1	£6	£12	£24/£36	
1825		£1	£6	£12	£24/£36	
1826		£2	£10	£30	£50/£75 \	
1826	(noted 1999)	- -	"gdEF"	£35	- - -/- - -	
1827		£1	£6	£12	£24/£36	
1828		£1	£6	£12	£24/£36	
1828	from Maundy proof set	- - -	- - -	- - -/- - -		
1829		£3	£9	£18	£36/£45	
1830		£2	£8	£16	£30/£40	

WILLIAM IV

SILVER 16mm

Date	Mintage	Fine	V.F.	E.F.	Unc	abt. FDC
1831	from Maundy set	£1	£10	£20	£30/£50	
1831	from proof set	- -	- - -	- - -	£50/£65	
1832	from Maundy set	£1	£10	£20	£21/£36	
1833	from Maundy set	£1	£10	£20	£21/£36	

For use in West Indies - unpolished surface:

Date	Mintage	Fine	V.F.	E.F.	Unc	abt. FDC
1834	401,016	£3	£15	£35	£70/£100	
1835	491,040	£3	£15	£30	£65/£95	
1836	411,840	£3	£15	£35	£70/£90	
1837	42,768	£5	£20	£45	£90/£125	

VICTORIA

Young Head as Maundy but 'dull' surface

Date	Mintage	Fine	V.F.	E.F.	Unc	abt. FDC
1838	1,203,840	£3	£8	£40	£60/£90	
1838	BRITANNIAB	extremely rare	- - - -	- - -/- - -		
1839	570,240	£3	£9	£45	£90/£120	
1839	Proof (from proof Maundy Set)	- - -	£200			
1840	633,600	£3	£9	£45	£90/£120	
1841	443,520	£4	£10	£45	£90/£120	
1842	2,027,520	£4	£10	£45	£90/£120	
1843	included above	£2	£6	£30	£60/£95	
1844	1,045,400	£2	£10	£40	£80/£110	

Preceding coins were for use only in the colonies.

Date	Mintage	Fine	V.F.	E.F.	Unc	abt. FDC
1845	1,314,720	£3	£9	£25	£50/£70	
1846	47,520	£15	£30	£120	£250/- - -	
1847	(Spink 2000)	- -	- - -	£350	- - -/- - -	
1848	(Spink 2000)	£40	£125	£325	- - -/- - -	
1849	126,720	£4	£12	£50	£75/£100	
1850	950,400	£4	£10	£25	£50/£80	
1851	479,065	£4	£10	£30	£60/£100	
1851	5 struck over 8	£8	£20	£60	£120/£200	

For a coin valued/costing less than £1, it should be borne in mind that almost ALL the value/cost lies in the handling, listing and storing of that coin. Whilst it enables collections to be expanded; such a small sum, even multiplied by many coins, is unlikely to be recoverable by re-selling. A long life, however, could make all the difference and we wish you exactly that!

THREEPENCES

VICTORIA
Young Head as Maundy but 'dull' surface

Date	Mintage	Fine	V.F.	E.F.	abt. Unc/FDC.
1852	(Coincraft Cat '95)	£50	£100	£250	- - - / - - -
1853	31,680	£15	£30	£120	£200/ - - -
1854	1,467,246	£4	£8	£30	£50/£75
1855	383,350	£4	£9	£35	£80/ - - -
1856	1,013,760	£4	£9	£35	£80/ - - -
1857	1,758,240	£4	£9	£35	£80/ - - -
1858	1,441,440	£4	£8	£35	£70/£95
1858	BRITANNIAB	£30	£120	£250	- - - / - - -
1859	3,579,840	£3	£6	£25	£40/£60
1860	3,405,600	£4	£9	£35	£60/£95
1861	3,294,720	£3	£6	£25	£45/£70
1862	1,156,320	£3	£8	£30	£60/£90
1863	950,400	£3	£8	£30	£65/£95
1864	1,330,560	£3	£6	£25	£40/£60
1865	1,742,400	£3	£8	£35	£70/£95
1866	1,900,800	£3	£6	£25	£40/£60
1867	712,800	£3	£7	£30	£50/£75
1868	1,457,280	£3	£6	£25	£40/£60
1868	RRITANNIAR	£20	£60	£200	- - - / - - -
1868	Laureate Head pattern by Wyon			- - -	- - - / - - -
1869	4,488 Maundy	£6	£12	£55	£95/ - - -
1870	1,283,218	£1/£3	£6	£25	£35/£60
1871	999,633	£1/£3	£6	£30	£45/£70
1872	1,293,271	£1/£3	£6	£30	£45/£70
1873	4,055,550	£1/£3	£5	£15	£30/£45
1874	4,427,031	£1/£3	£5	£15	£30/£45
1875	3,306,500	£1/£3	£5	£15	£30/£45
1876	1,834,389	£1/£3	£5	£15	£30/£45
1877	2,622,393	£1/£3	£5	£15	£30/£45
1878	2,419,975	£1/£3	£5	£15	£30/£45
1879	3,140,265	£1/£3	£5	£15	£30/£45
1880	1,610,069	£1/£3	£6	£18	£35/£50
1881	3,248,265	£1/£3	£6	£18	£35/£50
1882	472,965	£1/£4	£15	£25	£45/£70
1883	4,365,971	£1/£3	£5	£15	£30/£45
1884	3,322,424	£1/£3	£5	£15	£30/£45
1885	5,183,653	£1/£3	£5	£15	£30/£45
1886	6,152,669	£1/£3	£5	£15	£30/£45
1887	2,780,761 YOUNG	£1/£3	£5	£15	£30/£45
	Young Head proof		- - -	- - -	£200/ - -

Jubilee Head

1887	Included above	£2	£4	£6	£8/£12
1887	Jubilee Head proof	- - -	- - -		£35/£45
1888	518,199	£2	£4	£8	£15/£25
1889	4,587,010	£2	£4	£6	£12/£20
1890	4,465,834	£2	£4	£6	£12/£20
1891	6,323,027	£2	£4	£6	£12/£20
1892	2,578,226	£2	£4	£6	£12/£20
1893	3,067,243 JUBILEE	£8	£25	£75	£125/£175

Date	Mintage	Fine	V.F.	E.F.	abt. Unc/FDC.

VICTORIA

SILVER 16mm

Old or Widow Head

Date	Mintage	Fine	V.F.	E.F.	abt. Unc/FDC.
1893	Included above	£2	£4	£6	£12/£18
1893	1,312 Proofs	--	---	---	£30/£40
1893	(noted 1999)	--	---	"FDC"	£45
1894	1,608,603	£3	£5	£8	£15/£20
1895	4,788,609	£3	£5	£8	£15/£20
1896	4,598,442	£3	£5	£8	£15/£20
1897	4,541,294	£2	£4	£6	£12/£18
1898	4,567,177	£2	£4	£6	£12/£18
1899	6,246,281	£2	£4	£6	£12/£18
1900	10,644,480	£2	£4	£6	£12/£18
1901	6,098,400	£1	£3	£5	£10/£15

★ Threepences bearing dates not listed are, probably, Maundy pieces.

EDWARD VII

SILVER 16mm

Date	Mintage	Fine	V.F.	E.F.	abt. Unc/FDC.
1902	8,268,480	£1	£2	£5	£10/--
1902	15,123 proofs		---		£10/£15
1903	5,227,200	£2	£6	£22	£40/£50
1904	3,627,360	£3	£8	£25	£40/£60
1905	3,548,160	£3	£8	£20	£35/£45
1906	3,152,160	£2	£8	£20	£35/£45
1907	4,831,200	£1	£3	£9	£15/£25
1908	8,157,600	£2	£4	£12	£20/£30
1909	4,055,040	£2	£4	£12	£20/£30
1910	4,563,380	£1	£3	£9	£15/£25

GEORGE V

SILVER (.925 to 1920 then .500) 16mm

Date	Mintage	Fine	V.F.	E.F.	abt. Unc/FDC.
1911	5,841,084	75p	£2	£4	£9/£15
1911	6,001 proofs		---	---	£20
1912	8,932,825	60p	£1	£3	£8/£14
1913	7,143,242	60p	£1	£3	£8/£14
1914	6,733,584	60p	£1	£3	£8/£14
1915	5,450,617	60p	£2	£4	£8/£15
1916	18,555,201	60p	£1	£3	£6/£9
1917	21,662,490	60p	£1	£2	£4/£6
1918	20,630,909	60p	£1	£2	£4/£6
1919	16,845,687	60p	£1	£2	£4/£6
1920	16,703,597	50p	£1	£2	£4/£6
1920	.500 silver	50p	£1	£3	£7/£12
1921	8,749,301	50p	£1	£3	
1922	7,979,998	50p	£1	£6	£12/£20
1923	Small number of patterns, struck in nickel				
1923	Trial with "MODEL" obv. (auc. 2000)				£460
1925	3,731,859	£1	£2	£6	£12/£18
1925	Patterns, in nickel, of new (1927) design				--
1926	4,107,910	£1	£3	£12	£25/£32
1926	Modified Effigy	50p	£1	£5	£18/£25
1927	15,022 proofs oak sprig/acorn reverse				£25/£35
1928	1,302,106	£1	£2	£10	£20/£30
1929	None	---	---	---	---/---

THREEPENCES

GEORGE V

Date	Mintage	Fine	V.F.	E.F	Unc/abt. FDC
1930	1,319,412	50p	£1	£10	£20/£30
1930	(noted 1999)	- - -	- - -	"FDC"	- - -/£22
1931	6,251,936	50p	£1	£2	£4/£6
1932	5,887,325	50p	£1	£2	£3/£4
1933	5,578,541	50p	£1	£2	£3/£4
1934	7,405,954	50p	£1	£2	£4/£6
1934	A proof offered for sale in 1976 (!)				/£55
1934	Proof (listed in Coincraft Cat. 1997)				£250
1935	7,027,654	25p	50p	£1	£3/£4
1936	3,238,670	25p	50p	£1	£2/£3

EDWARD VIII   (Duke of Windsor)

1937	Pattern bearing a design of three rings, "guesstimate"		£9500/£12000
1937	Silver 'thrift plant' proof by Maklouf	"FDC"	£20
1937	Silver 'ER monogram' proof by Maklouf	"FDC"	£16

GEORGE VI   SILVER (50%) 16mm

Date	Mintage	Fine	V.F.	E.F	Unc/abt. FDC
1937	8,148,156	25p	50p	£1	£2/£3
1937	26,402 proofs	- - -	- - -	- - -	£3/£5
1938	6,402,473	25p	50p	£2	£4/£6
1939	1,355,860	25p	50p	£3	£6/£9
1940	7,914,401	25p	50p	£1	£2/£3
1941	7,979,411	25p	50p	£1	£2/£3
1942	4,144,051 Colonial	£1	£2	£5	£9/£15
1943	1,379,220 Colonial	£2	£3	£6	£12/£20
1944	2,005,553 Colonial	£3	£7	£12	£24/£35
1945	371,000 dated 1944; re-melted by The Mint				
1945	An "Escapee"			(Coincraft '97 VF £4,000)	

ELIZABETH II

Date	Mintage	Fine	V.F.	E.F	Unc/abt. FDC
1953	Maundy Silver 3d	- -	£25	£30	£60/- - -
1954 to 1970		- -	£8	£12	£15/- - -
1970 to 1997		- -	- -	£12	£15/- - -

NICKEL-BRASS THREEPENCES   DODECAGONAL

EDWARD VIII Duke of Windsor

1937 Date divided by THRIFT PLANT (Sea-pink); a few were made for slot machine
       testing and thicknesses vary.

	Spinks (1990)	£28,500
	Cooke (1994)	£24,500

1937 Date at bottom, but effigy Edward VIII.   Coincraft (1999) £20,000

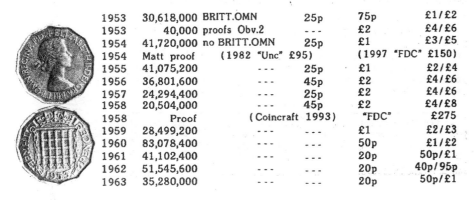

Date	Mintage	Fine	V.F.	E.F.	Unc/abt FDC
GEORGE VI	MODIFIED THRIFT PLANT				
1937	45,707,957	- - -	50p	£1	£2/£3
1937	(Welsh 1996)	- - -		"Gem, BU/FDC"	- - /£4
1937	26,402 proofs	- - -	- - -	£3	£6/£9
1938	14,532,332	5p	50p	£3	£6/£9
1939	5,603,021	12p	£1	£4	£15/£20
1940	12,636,018	10p	£1	£2	£4/£6
1941	60,239,489	- - -	£1	£2	£3/£4
1942	103,214,400	- - -	£1	£2	£3/£4
1943	101,702,400	- - -	£1	£2	£3/£4
1944	69,760,000	- - -	£1	£2	£3/£4
1945	33,942,466	- - -	£1	£3	£5/£8
1946	620,734	£1	£10	£40	£125/£200
1946	(noted 1999)	- - -	"gd.E.F."	£70	- - - - / - - - -
1946	Proof	"FDC" (1985)	£250	- - -	(1999) £360
1947	None	- - -	- - -	- - -	- - - -
1948	4,230,400	12p	£1	£5	£15/£20
	IND. IMP discontinued				
1949	464,000	£2	£10	£60	£120/£160
1949	A proof in brass	- - -	- - -	- - -	£200/£400
1950	1,600,000	10p	£3	£15	£30/£50
1950	17,513 proofs	- - -	- - -	- - -	£15/£25
1951	1,184,000	10p	£3	£18	£40/£60
1951	20,000 proofs	- - -	- - -	- - -	£25/£30
1952	25,494,400	- - -		£1	£2	£3/£4

British Museum has proof/s of each date

1937   Two different spacings from rim of word THREE noted :
               Rev. A = large gap;   Rev. B = small gap

Sharp v Rounded Corners:
1937 - 1940 All sharp
1941 - Both
1942 - 1946 All rounded
1948 - Both
1949 - All rounded
1950 - 1952 All sharp

Tiny initials of designers:
H.P. = T. Humphrey Paget
K.G. = Kruger Gray
W.P. = Wilson Parker
M.G. = Mary Gillick
W.G.= William Gardner

ELIZABETH II PORTCULLIS with CHAINS, ROYALLY CROWNED

1953	30,618,000	BRITT.OMN	25p	75p	£1/£2
1953	40,000	proofs Obv.2	- - -	£2	£4/£6
1954	41,720,000	no BRITT.OMN	25p	£1	£3/£5
1954	Matt proof	(1982 "Unc" £95)		(1997 "FDC" £150)	
1955	41,075,200	- - -	25p	£1	£2/£4
1956	36,801,600	- - -	45p	£2	£4/£6
1957	24,294,400	- - -	25p	£2	£4/£6
1958	20,504,000	- - -	45p	£2	£4/£8
1958	Proof	(Coincraft 1993)		"FDC"	£275
1959	28,499,200	- - -	- - -	£1	£2/£3
1960	83,078,400	- - -	- - -	50p	£1/£2
1961	41,102,400	- - -	- - -	20p	50p/£1
1962	51,545,600	- - -	- - -	20p	40p/95p
1963	35,280,000	- - -	- - -	20p	50p/£1

Date	Mintage	Fine	V.F.	E.F.	Unc/abt FDC

ELIZABETH II continued

Date	Mintage	Fine	V.F.	E.F.	Unc/abt FDC
1963	35,280,000	---	---	20p	50p/£1
1964	44,867,200	---	---	10p	50p/75p
1965	27,160,000	---	---	10p	50p/75p
1966	53,760,000	---	---	10p	20p/50p
1967	151,780,800	---	---	5p	10p/25p
1970	750,476	proofs for LAST STERLING set			£2/£3
Undated error - double obverse ("heads" both sides)					£350

V.A.T., not included here, is sometimes
absorbed by the seller on a 'special offer' basis.

1953 (a) = I of ELIZABETH points to corner of rim/edge.
     (b) = I is much further to the right (see page 12).

1953 Obv. 1 Details, particularly head ribbon and initials M.G. are
         poorly defined = ex-specimen set (page 55).
     Obv. 2 Portrait more sharply outlined as are the ends of
         the head ribbon = normal issue. Both have ovoid stops.

1954 Much sharper overall and with round stops.

FOURPENCES or GROATS

Date	Mintage	Fair/Fine	V.F.	E.F.	abt. Unc./FDC

WILLIAM IV Reverse has FOUR PENCE in words - SILVER 16mm

Date	Mintage	Fair/Fine	V.F.	E.F.	abt. Unc./FDC
1836	Britannia seated : D :	£2/£5	£10	£20	£40/£60
1836	Colons close to :D:	£5	£20	£40	---/---
1836	Proofs, grained (milled) edge in silver		---	---/£200	
1836	Proofs, plain edge in gold	(Coincraft Cat '99)		£4,000	
1836	Proofs, plain edge in silver		---	£275	---/£350
1836	Proof, in silver on thin flan		---	---	---/£600
1837	962,280	£3/£6	£15	£30	£45/£65

A number of patterns exist

The FOURPENCE, not the silver threepence, is the true "Joey": taking
its name from one Joseph Hume who recommended it to facilitate
payment of the, then, 4d London omnibus fare. Following a 'nudge'
from Mike Smith we feel that this quotation should read "4d London
Hackney Carriage fare".

Date	Mintage		Fair/Fine	V.F.	E.F.	abt. Unc./FDC
VICTORIA		FOUR PENCE in words -			SILVER 16mm	
1837	Proof only - plain edged		---			--- /£1200
1837	Proof only - grained (milled) edge			---		--- /£1200
1838	2,150,280		£4	£8	£20	£36/£50
1838	2nd 8 struck over ∞		£10	£20	£40	£60/£95
1838	Plain edged proof		---	---	---	£150
1839	1,461,240		£1/£3	£6	£18	£36/£50
1839	Plain edged proof from the sets		↑↑	---		£150
1839	Obverse/Reverse alignment		↑↓	---		£200
1840	1,496,880:					
	Large date		£3/£6	£12	£18	£36/£50
	Small date		£3/£6	£15	£25	£40/£60
1840	1840 struck over O	1840	(source Mason 1994)			--- / ---
1841	344,520		£4	£8	£20	£40/£60
1841	Second 1 over I		£4	£8	£20	£40/£60
1842	724,680		£1/£3	£6	£12	£36/£50
1842	Plain edged proof		---	---	---	£200
1842	2 struck over 1		£5	£10	£50	-- / -- --
1843	1,817,640		£2	£6	£18	£36/£54
1844	855,360		£2	£6	£20	£50/£70
1845	914,760		£2	£6	£20	£50/£65
1846	1,366,200		£2	£15	£30	£60/£85
1847	7 struck over 6		£15	£60	£240	--- / -- --
1848	712,800		£5	£10	£20	£40/£60
1848	2nd 8 over 6		£6	£12	£30	£60/£80
1848	2nd 8 over 7		£6	£15	£40	£75/£95
1849	380,160		£4	£9	£25	£40/£60
1849	9 struck over 8		£5	£10	£30	£60/£80
1851	594,000		£15	£50	£150	£300/ -- --
1852	31,300		£25	£90	£200	£400/ -- --
1853	11,880		£30	£120	£300	£600/ -- --
1853	Grained (milled) edge proof from set			---		£300
1853	Plain edged proof (noted 1998)		"EF" ·	£155		-- --
1854	1,096,613		£2	£5	£15	£25/£36
1854	5 struck over 3		£2/£3	£15	£30	£60/£85
1855	646,041		£2/£5	£10	£20	£40/£60
1857	Proof only, grained edge		---	---		£650
1862	Proof only, plain edge		---	---		£550
1862	Proof only, grained edge	--	---	---		£550
1888	JUBILEE HEAD (Br.Guiana)	£4	£8	£25		£50/£65
1888	Grained edge proof		---	---		£400/£500

Date	Mintage/etc (ESC)	Fair/Fine	V.F.	E.F.	Unc/abt. FDC

GEORGE IV   SILVER 19mm

Date	Mintage/etc (ESC)	Fair/Fine	V.F.	E.F.	Unc/abt. FDC
1820	Proof only, garnished shield	---			£600/£750
1821	863,280	£8	£22	£60	£125/£200
1821	Proof (1655)	---	---	---	----/£350
1821	BBITANNIAR error	£40	£120	£500	£700/£950
1824	633,600 gartered shield	£10	£20	£60	£120/£170
1825	483,120 gartered shield	£8	£18	£45	£80/£120
1825	Pattern for BARE HEAD design (Spink)				£2,000
1826	689,040	£15	£50	£125	£250/£325
1826	A proof - Shield within Garter			---	£125/£250

Type change to BARE HEAD - LION-on-CROWN reverse

Date	Mintage/etc (ESC)	Fair/Fine	V.F.	E.F.	Unc/abt. FDC
1826	Included above	£5	£15	£45	£90/£125
1826	A proof - Bare Head/Lion on Crown				----/£150
1827	166,320	£12	£30	£80	£165/£220
1828	15,840 ?	£4/£9	£24	£85	£130/----
1829	403,920	£4/£9	£20	£80	£125/----

WILLIAM IV   SILVER 19mm

Date	Mintage/etc (ESC)	Fair/Fine	V.F.	E.F.	Unc/abt. FDC
1831	1,340,195 (1670)	£6	£18	£55	£95/£150
1831	A proof - plain edge	(noted 2000) "abt. FDC"			£160
1831	A proof with grained edge	---	---		£350
1831	A proof in palladium	---	---		£1,500
1834	5,892,480	£4	£15	£40	£80/£120
1835	1,552,320	£4	£15	£40	£90/£130
1836	1,987,920	£12	£30	£90	£120/£160
1837	506,880	£15	£35	£100	£150/£200

VICTORIA   Young Head

Date	Mintage/etc (ESC)	Fair/Fine	V.F.	E.F.	Unc/abt. FDC
1838	1,607,760	£4	£12	£45	£75/£110
1839	3,310,560	£4	£15	£50	£75/£120
1839	A proof or pattern	(noted 2000) "abt. FDC"			£250
1840	2,098,800	£5	£9	£38	£75/£110
1840	Pattern by W.Wyon rev cancelled with fine lines				---/---
1841	1,386,000	£5	£18	£60	£95/£150
1841	Pattern,	gold, using half-sovereign reverse			
1842	601,920	£5	£18	£60	£90/£130
1843	3,160,080	£4	£15	£50	£80/£120
1844	3,975,840	£4	£12	£40	£70/£100
1844	Has large 44	£7	£20	£75	£120/---
1845	3,714,480	£5	£15	£50	£90/£140
1846	4,268,880	£5	£10	£45	£70/£90
1848	586,080	£30	£90	£300	£500/£600
1848	8 struck over 6	£30	£90	£300	£500/£600
1848	8 struck over 7	£30	£90	£300	£500/£600
1850	498,960	£5	£15	£50	£100/£150
1850	5 struck over 3 (Cooke 1998)		£35	"gdVF/VF"	
1851	2,288,107	£5	£15	£40	£80/£120
1851	'Doubling' DEI/	--	---	"BU"	£125
1852	904,586	£5	£15	£50	£90/£125

SIXPENCES

Date	Mintage/etc (ESC)	Fair/Fine	V.F.	E.F.	Unc/abt. FDC
VICTORIA	**Young Head**				
1853	53 higher (noted 2000)	---		£55	---/ ---
1853	3,837,930	£5	£15	£45	£80/£120
1853	A proof	---	---	---	"FDC" £250
1854	840,116	£60	£250	£600	£1000/£1500
1855	1,129,084	£5	£15	£45	£90/£125
1855	A proof	---	---	---	£250
1856	2,779,920	£5	£15	£45	£95/£125
1856	A pattern	worded	HALF SHILLING		----
1856	A pattern	worded	1/2 SHILLING		----
1857	2,233,440	£5	£12	£40	£80/£120
1858	1,932,480	£5	£12	£40	£80/£120
1858	A Proof	---	---	---	£250
1859	4,688,640	£5	£12	£45	£90/£125
1859	9 struck over 8 (Spink 1988 GEF £145)				---/ ---
1860	1,100,880	£5	£12	£42	£75/£120
1862	990,000	£25	£90	£300	£500/£600
1863	491,040	£15	£60	£200	£300/£375

1856	Variety: longer line below PENCE - rare
1857	Variety: longer line below PENCE - rare

NOW WITH DIE NUMBER (above date, below wreath)

Date	Mintage/etc	Fair/Fine	V.F.	E.F.	Unc/abt. FDC
1864	4,253,040	£5	£15	£50	£95/£130
1865	1,631,520	£5	£15	£50	£100/£150
1866	5,140,080	£4	£12	£45	£90/£125
1866	No die number	£20	£100	£200	----/£500
1867	1,362,240	£6	£18	£60	£95/ ---
1867	A proof	---	---	---	£250
1868	1,069,200	£6	£20	£65	£95/£145
1869	388,080	£6	£20	£65	£95/£145
1869	A proof	---	---	---	£500/----
1870	479,613	£5	£20	£80	£120/£150
1870	A proof	---	---	---	£250
1871	3,662,684	£6	£20	£45	£60/ £90
1871	A proof (noted 1996) "Plain edged Uncirc."				£800/ ---
1871	No die number	£6	£20	£50	£85/£125
1871	A proof without die number		---		£250/£500
1872	3,382,048 die no.	£4	£10	£30	£60/ £90
1873	4,594,733 die no.	£6	£15	£35	£65/ £95
1874	4,225,726 die no.	£4	£10	£30	£60/ £90
1875	3,256,545 die no.	£4	£10	£30	£60/ £90
1876	841,435 die no.	£6	£15	£55	£100/£150
1877	4,066,486 die no.	£4	£10	£40	£75/£100
1877	No die number	£5	£12	£40	£75/£100
1878	2,624,525 die no.	£4	£10	£40	£75/£100
1878	A proof of previous coin	---	---		£250/£400
1878	8 struck over 7 (die no.)	£20	£75	£250	----/----
1878	DRITANNIAR error	£50	£150	£250	£375/£575
1878	(noted 2001)	£45	"nearFine" ----		----/----
1879	3,326,313	£6	£15	£55	£100/£150

SIXPENCES

VICTORIA   Young Head

DIE NUMBERS DISCONTINUED

Date	Mintage/etc	Fine	V.F.	E.F.	abt. Unc/FDC
1879	Included above	£4	£12	£35	£65/ £95
1879	A proof	---	---	---	£200/£400
1880	Hair lock on cheek	£8	£15	£50	£100/£150
1880	No lock of hair ★	£4	£10	£25	£50/£75
1880	No lock of hair ★ ★	(Mason 2000) "BU"			---/ £60
	★ ★ The reverse of this example has smaller lettering than ★				
1880	A proof	---	---	---	£150/£300
1881	6,239,447	£4	£10	£20	£40/ £65
1881	A proof	---	---	---	£175/£250
1882	759,809	£6	£18	£50	£100/£125
1883	4,986,558	£4	£10	£20	£40/ £65
1884	3,422,565	£4	£10	£20	£40/ £65
1884	Pattern bearing national emblems			---	£600
1885	4,652,771	£4	£10	£20	£40/ £65
1886	2,728,249	£4	£12	£35	£50/ £80
1886	A proof	---	---	---	£175/£200
1887	3,675,607 Young Head	£4	£9	£18	£32/£50
1887	A proof Young Head	---	---	---	£120/£175

> First Young Head 1838 to 1866 inclusive.
> Second Young Head 1867 to 1880; as first but lower relief.
> Third Young Head 1880 to 1887; Reverse has larger letters.

Jubilee Head

Reverse   A--- GARTERED SHIELD 'WITHDRAWN':

1887	3,675,607	£1	£3	£5	£8/£15
1887	JEB on truncation £10/£15	£30	£75	£125/£200
1887	R of Victoria struck over V (or I)		£75	£125/£200
1887	Proof Gartered Shield		---	£50/£75

Being the same size and design as the half-sovereign many were gold plated and passed as such. This led to the withdrawal of this design of sixpence.

A---

1887	Pattern - Gartered Shield - date above crown

Reverse --B-- CROWNED VALUE IN WREATH:

1887	Included above	£1	£2	£6	£9/£12
1887	Proof Crowned Value in Wreath		---	£60/£90
1887	Patterns by Spink, Lion-Shield-Unicorn Reverse: in gold, brass, copper, tin and aluminium.				

B---

1888	4,197,698	£1/£3	£6	£12	£20/£30
1888	A proof	---	---	---	£115
1889	8,738,928	£1/£3	£6	£12	£20/£30
1890	9,386,955	£1/£3	£6	£14	£28/£42
1890	A proof	---	---	---	£115
1891	7,022,734	£1/£2	£5	£12	£24/£30
1892	6,245,746	£1/£2	£5	£10	£20/£30
1893	7,350,619	£50/£100	£300	£950	£1500/----

SIXPENCES

VICTORIA Old or Widow Head

Date	Mintage	Fair/Fine	V.F.	E.F.	abt. Unc./Unc.
1893	Included above	£1/£2	£5	£12	£20/£30
1893	A proof	- - -	- - -	£20	£40/£60
1894	3,467,704	£1/£3	£5	£16	£30/£40
1895	7,024,631	£1/£2	£5	£15	£30/£40
1896	6,651,699	£1/£2	£5	£15	£30/£40
1897	5,031,498	£1/£2	£5	£15	£30/£40
1898	5,914,100	£1/£2	£5	£16	£30/£45
1899	7,996,804	£1/£2	£5	£15	£30/£40
1900	8,984,354	£2/£4	£10	£20	£35/£50
1901	5,108,757	£1/£2	£5	£12	£20/£30

> The sixpence became known as a "TANNER". The cab fare from the City of London to Tanner's Hill cost sixpence.
> "A Tanner One"

EDWARD VII
CROWNED SIXPENCE WITHIN WREATH · ·925 SILVER 19mm

1902	6,367,378	£3	£6	£15	£25/£30
1902	15,123 proofs with matt finish				FDC £30
1903	5,410,096	£2	£8	£20	£40/£60
1904	4,487,098	£5	£12	£35	£65/£90
1904	(noted 1999)	- - -	"UNC"	£80/- - -	
1905	4,235,556	£4	£10	£25	£50/£70
1906	7,641,146	£3	£8	£20	£45/£65
1906	(noted 2000)	- -	- -	"abt. Unc"	£45/- - -
1907	8,733,673	£3	£8	£20	£45/£65
1908	6,739,491	£3	£9	£25	£50/£75
1909	6,584,017	£2	£8	£20	£40/£60
1910	12,490,724	£2	£5	£15	£20/£30
1910	(noted 1998)	- -	- -	"BU.FDC"	- - -/£35
1910	(noted 2001)	- -	- -	"abt.Unc"	£26/- - -

GEORGE V LION ON CROWN · SILVER 19mm ·925 until 1920

1911	9,155,310	£1	£4	£10	£20/£25
1911	6,007 proofs	- -	- - -	- - -	£22/£30
1911	(noted 1998 and 2000) proof			"FDC"	- - -/£35
1912	10,984,129	£1	£2	£20	£35/£50
1913	7,499,833	£1	£4	£15	£32/£45
1914	22,714,602	£1	£2	£5	£9/£15
1915	15,694,597	£1	£2	£5	£9/£15
1916	22,207,178	£1	£2	£5	£9/£15
1917	7,725,475	£1	£2	£12	£24/£36
1918	27,558,743	£1	£2	£9	£12/£18
1919	13,375,447	£1	£2	£8	£18/£25
1920	14,136,287:				
1920	Silver .925	£2	£5	£15	£30/£45

> MODIFIED EFFIGY : In the absence of a direct comparison, the modified effigy (or modified head) can be distinguished by the initials which appear on the truncation of the neck. Before modification, the initials B.M. are placed near the centre of truncation. After modification they appear, *without stops*, well to the right thus: BM (not B.M.) The initials are those of the designer of the coin: Bertram Mackennal.

38 SIXPENCES

Date	Mintage	Fine	V.F.	E.F.	abt. Unc/ FDC

GEORGE V LION ON CROWN · SILVER 19mm ·925 until 1920

Date	Mintage	Fine	V.F.	E.F.	abt. Unc/FDC
1920	Silver .500	£1	£2	£8	£15/£24
1921	30,339,741	£1	£2	£6	£12/£24
1921	(noted 1999)	---	---	"Choice BU"	---/£26
1922	16,878,890	£1	£2	£7	£15/£24
1923	6,382,793	£2	£4	£15	£35/£50
1924	17,444,218	£1	£3	£8	£16/£25
1925	12,720,558	£1	£2	£6	£12/£20
1925	With new broader rim		£2	£10	£20/£30
1925	A pattern of the 1928 design in nickel				£450
1926	21,809,261	£1	£2	£10	£20/£30
1926	Modified Effigy	£1	£3	£8	£12/£18
1927	68,939,873	£1	£2	£5	£9/£15
1927	15,000 proofs Rev. new OAK/ACORN design				£20/£25
1928	23,123,384	---	£1	£5	£9/£12
1929	28,319,326	---	£1	£3	£6/£12
1930	16,990,289	---	£1	£3	£7/£10
1931	16,873,268 ★	---	£2	£4	£7/£12
1931	A proof ★	---	---	---	£175
1932	9,406,117 ★	---	£4	£8	£15/£25
1933	22,185,083 ★	---	£2	£5	£10/£15
1933	A proof ★	---	---	---	£180
1934	9,304,009 ★	---	£2	£5	£10/£15
1935	13,995,621 ★	---	£1	£4	£8/£12
1936	24,380,171 ★	---	£1	£3	£8/£12

★ these have a finer grained (milled) edge

EDWARD VIII (Duke of Windsor)
SIX LINKED RINGS of ST. EDWARD

1937	(noted 1989)	---	---	"abt.FDC"	£9,500
1937	(noted 1996)	---	---	"abt.FDC"	£11,000
1937	(noted 1997)	---	---	"abt.FDC"	£12,000

LION on CROWN

1937	Sterling silver proof by Maklouf	"FDC"	£20

GEORGE VI 50% SILVER, 50% ALLOY to 1946 · 19mm

1937	22,302,524	---	25p	£2	£3/ £5
1937	26,402 proofs	---	---		£3/ £5
1938	13,402,701	---	---	£3	£6/£12
1939	28,670,304	---	---	£2	£3/ £4
1940	20,875,196	---	---	£2	£3/ £4
1941	23,186,616	---	---	£2	£3/ £4
1942	44,942,785	---	---	£1	£2/ £3
1943	46,927,111	---	---	£1	£2/ £3
1944	37,952,600	---	---	£1	£3/ £4
1945	39,939,259	---	---	£1	£3/ £4
1946	43,466,407	---	---	£1	£2/ £3

CUPRO-NICKEL

1946	Proof, for new coinage, in cupro-nickel	/£400
1947	29,993,263 --- --- £1	£2/ £4
1948		

SIXPENCES

GEORGE VI   CUPRO-NICKEL

Monogram GRI was changed to GRVI in 1949 when title IND: IMP: (INDAE IMPERATOR) - Emperor of India - discontinued

Date	Mintage		Fine	V.F.	E.F.	abt.Unc/FDC
1949	41,355,515	---		---	£1	£3/ £5
1950	32,741,955	---		---	£2	£6/ £9
1950	17,513	proofs		---	---	£6/ £9
1951	40,399,491	---		---	£1	£3/ £6
1951	20,000	proofs		---	---	£4/ £6
1952	1,013,477	£1		£4	£10	£30/£50
1952	Proof from polished dies	---			---	£750

ELIZABETH II   NATIONAL EMBLEMS INTERTWINED

1953	70,323,876		---	---	50p	£1/ £2
1953	40,000	proofs		---	---	£3/ £5

BRITT: OMN: discontinued

1954	105,241,150		---	---	£1	£2/ £4
1955	109,929,554		---	---	20p	£1/ £2
1956	109,841,555		---	---	20p	£1/ £2
1957	105,654,290		---	---	20p	£1/ £2
1958	123,518,527		---	---	---	£1/ £2
1959	93,089,441		---	---	---	50p / £1
1960	103,288,346		---	---	---	60p / £1
1961	115,052,017		---	---	---	60p / £1
1962	178,359,637		---	---	---	50p/ £1
1963	112,964,000		---	---	---	50p/ £1
1964	152,336,000		---	---	---	50p/ £1
1965	129,644,000		---	---	---	50p/ £1
1966	175,696,000		---	---	---	50p/ £1
1966	Struck in bronze	---		---	---	£150
1966	"Mule" with Commonwealth Portrait auction 1993 £396					
1967	240,788,000		---	---	---	---/20p
1970	750,476	proofs for LAST STERLING set £2/ £3				

Various 'pointings' have been noted:
1953
ELIZABETH
..
ELIZABETH
1955
SIXPENCE
.
SIXPENCE
..
1964 and 1965
. ..
REGINA - REGINA
Letters point TO or
BETWEEN rim beads

EIGHTPENCES and OCTORINOS

Date			V.F.	E.F.	abt. Unc./FDC

GEORGE V   ESC refers to Seaby's "The English Silver Coinage"

PATTERNS by HUTH   Central Star bears LEGS OF MAN

1913	ESC 1431A	Pattern for eightpence in copper			---
	ESC 1481	OCTORINO	---	---	£350/----
	ESC 1481	Noted (Seaby 1990) abt.FDC			£450
1913	ESC 1482	EIGHTPENCE in silver	---		----/£450
	ESC 1482A	EIGHT PENCE in copper	---		----
		(Spink 1980) in iron			£225/----.

These items appear only very rarely.

Young Head   Jubilee Head   "Gothic" Head

"Bun" Head   Old, Veiled or Widow Head

Gillick Head
(Mary Gillick)

Machin Head
(Arnold Machin)—

Maklouf Head
(Raphael Maklouf)

Rank-Broadley Head
(Ian Rank-Broadley)—

VICTORIA One Franc ONE FRANC/TEN PENCE   Silver 23mm

	E.F.	Unc./F.D.C.
1867 Pattern - ESC 1416	£400	£800/£1200

ROYAL MAUNDY

Briefly: specially struck silver coins are distributed to as many old men and women as the Monarch has years; those years being 'expressed' in pence. Thus, on the Monarch's fortieth birthday, 40 men and 40 women each receive 40 pence or four Maundy sets at tenpence per set. The following year the distribution would be to 41 men and 41 women: four sets plus an extra penny. There are additonal sums, paid in conventional notes and coins, in lieu of food and clothing. The distribution takes place on Maundy Thursday: the day before Good Friday.

MAUNDY SETS

FACE VALUE TEN PENCE THE SET OF FOUR COINS: 11mm · 13mm · 16mm · 18mm

Date		V.F.	E.F.	abt. Unc./FDC
GEORGE IV				
1822		£30	£70	£120/£150
1822	A proof set (ESC 2426)			£600
1823		£25	£80	£120/£145
1824		£30	£80	£125/£140
1825		£25	£60	£100/£125
1826		£25	£60	£100/£125
1827		£25	£85	£125/£150
1828		£25	£60	£100/£125
1828	A proof set (ESC 2433)			£750
1829		£25	£60	£100/£125
1830		£25	£85	£125/£150
WILLIAM IV				
1831		£35	£90	£175/£225
1831	Proof	- - -	- - -	£250/£450
1831	Proof in gold		- - -	£15,000
1832		£35	£80	£120/£150
1833		£35	£80	£120/£150
1834		£35	£80	£130/£200
1835		£35	£80	£120/£150
1836		£35	£90	£175/£225
1837		£35	£90	£175/£225

MAUNDY SETS

FACE VALUE TEN PENCE THE SET OF FOUR COINS: 11mm · 13mm · 16mm · 18mm

Young Head VICTORIA *Young Head*

Date	Sets	EF.	Unc/FDC	Date	Sets	EF.	Unc/FDC
1838	4,158	£35	£60/£90	1862	4,158	£36	£50/£65
1838	Proofs	- - -	£200	1863	4,158	£36	£50/£65
1838	Proofs in gold		£15,000	1864	4,158	£36	£50/£65
1839	4,125	£35	£60/£90	1865	4,158	£36	£50/£65
1839	Proofs	- - -	£250	1867	4,158	£36	£50/£65
1840	4,125	£35	£60/£95	1867	Proofs		£265
1841	2,574	£35	£65/£100	1868	4,158	£36	£50/£65
1842	4,125	£35	£60/£90	1869	4,158	£36	£50/£65
1843	4,158	£35	£60/£90	1870	4,488	£36	£50/£65
1844	4,158	£35	£60/£90	1871	4,488	£36	£50/£65
1845	4,158	£35	£60/£90	1871	Proof Auct.89		£410
1846	4,158	£35	£65/£100	1872	4,328	£36	£50/£65
1847	4,158	£35	£60/£90	1873	4,162	£36	£50/£65
1848	4,158	£35	£60/£90	1874	4,488	£36	£50/£65
1849	4,158	£42	£70/£110	1875	4,154	£36	£50/£65
1850	4,158	£35	£55/£70	1876	4,488	£36	£50/£65
1851	4,158	£35	£55/£70	1877	4,488	£36	£50/£65
1852	4,158	£35	£55/£70	1878	4,488	£36	£50/£65
1853	4,158	£35	£55/£70	1878	Proofs	£50	£200
1853	Proofs	- - -	£350/£500	1879	4,488	£36	£50/£65
1854	4,158	£36	£50/£65	1879	Proofs	- - -	£1,000
1855	4,158	£36	£50/£65	1880	4,488	£36	£50/£65
1856	4,158	£36	£50/£65	1881	Proofs	- - -	£200
1857	4,158	£36	£55/£70	1882	4,488	£36	£50/£65
1858	4,158	£36	£55/£70	1883	4,488	£36	£50/£65
1859	4,158	£36	£55/£70	1884	4,488	£36	£50/£65
1860	4,158	£36	£50/£65	1885	4,488	£36	£50/£65
1861	4,158	£36	£50/£65	1886	4,488	£36	£50/£65
				1887	4,488	£40	£55/£75

Jubilee Head

Date	Sets	EF.	Unc/FDC
1888	4,488	£36	£60/£75
1888	Proofs	- - -	- - -
1889	4,488	£45	£60/£75
1890	4,488	£45	£60/£75
1891	4,488	£45	£60/£75
1892	4,488	£45	£55/£70

Old or Widow Head

Date	Sets	EF.	Unc/FDC
1893	8,976	£25	£50/£65
1894	8,976	£25	£55/£60
1895	8,877	£25	£55/£60
1896	8,476	£25	£55/£65
1897	8,976	£20	£45/£60
1898	8,976	£35	£45/£60
1898★	(1994)	"FDC orig. case" £75	
1899	8,976	£35	£50/£75
1900	8,976	£50	£75/£100
1901	8,976	£30	£45/£60

Original Documentation Adds Value. Add £10/£15 for contemporary dated case.
1898★ No 'official' case but there were cases "of the time" by various institutions.

FACE VALUE TEN PENCE THE SET OF FOUR COINS: 11mm · 13mm · 16mm · 18mm

EDWARD VII

Date	Sets	EF.	F.D.C. from/to	Date	Sets	EF.	F.D.C. from/to
1902	8,976	£30	£55/£65	1906	8,800	£30	£45/£60
1902	"Choice orig. box"		£65	1906	Dated octagonal case		£8
1902	15,123 matt proofs		£50	1907	8,760	£30	£45/£60
1903	8,976	£30	£55/£65	1908	8,760	£30	£45/£60
1904	8,876	£30	£55/£65	1909	1,983	£35	£45/£65
1905	8,976	£30	£55/£65	1910	1,440	£40	£60/£70

GEORGE V

Date	Sets	EF.	Unc/FDC	Date	Sets	EF.	Unc/FDC
1911	1,768	£30	£55/£70	1924	1,515	£32	£55/£60
1911	proofs	---	£60	1925	1,438	£32	£55/£60
1912	1,246	£25	£55/£70	1926	1,504	£32	£55/£60
1913	1,228	£25	£55/£70	1927	1,647	£32	£55/£65
1914	982	£42	£55/£65	1928	1,642	£32	£52/£62
1915	1,293	£25	£55/£70	1929	1,761	£32	£55/£60
1916	1,128	£25	£55/£70	1930	1,724	£32	£55/£60
1917	1,237	£25	£55/£70	1931	1,759	£32	£55/£60
1918	1,375	£30	£55/£70	1932	1,835	£32	£55/£60
1919	1,258	£25	£50/£60	1933	1,872	£32	£55/£60
1920	1,399	£25	£55/£80	1934	1,887	£32	£55/£60
1921	1,386	£25	£55/£65	1935	1,928	£30	£55/£65
1922	1,373	£75	£100/£150	1936	1,323	£35	£60/£75
1923	1,430	£35	£55/£70	Orig. Documents Add Value			

GEORGE VI

Date	Sets	abt Unc/FDC	Date	Sets	abt Unc/FDC
1937	1,325	£30/£40	1945	1,355	£30/£40
1938	1,275	£30/£40	1946	1,365	£30/£40
1939	1,234	£30/£40	1947	1,375	£30/£40
1940	1,277	£30/£40	1948	1,385	£30/£40
1941	1,253	£30/£40	1949	1,395	£30/£40
1942	1,231	£30/£40	1950	1,405	£30/£40
1943	1,239	£30/£40	1951	1,468	£30/£40
1944	1,259	£30/£40	1952	1,012	£40/£50

1936		distributed by Edward VIII
1937	to 1946	.500 silver was used.
1947	to 1952	a return to Sterling silver
1949	to 1952	a change of inscription
1952		distributed by Queen Elizabeth.
1954	to 1970	a change of inscription

MAUNDY SETS

11mm · 13mm · 16mm · 18mm

Date	Complete Sets		Unc / FDC
ELIZABETH II			
1953	1,025	St.Paul's Cathedral	£200 / £300
1953	In gold	--- (1985)	£5,750
1954	1,020	Westminster Abbey	£35 / £45
1955	1,036	Southwark Cathedral	£35 / £45
1956	1,088	Westminster Abbey	£35 / £45
1957	1,094	St.Alban's Cathedral	£35 / £45
1958	1,100	Westminster Abbey	£40 / £50
1959	1,106	Windsor	£40 / £50
1960	1,112	Westminster Abbey	£40 / £50
1961	1,118	Rochester Cathedral	£40 / £50
1962	1,125	Westminster Abbey	£40 / £50
1963	1,131	Chelmsford	£40 / £50
1964	1,137	Westminster	£40 / £50
1965	1,143	Canterbury	£40 / £50
1966	1,206	Westminster	£40 / £50
1967	986	Durham	£40 / £50
1968	964	Westminster	£40 / £50
1969	1,002	Selby	£40 / £50
1970	980	Westminster	£40 / £50

NOW DECIMAL PENCE

Date	Complete Sets			Unc / FDC
1971	1,018	Tewkesbury Abbey		£40 / £50
1972	1,026	York Minster		£45 / £55
1973	1,004	Westminster		£45 / £55
1974	1,042	Salisbury		£45 / £55
1975	1,050	Peterborough		£45 / £55
1976	1,158	Hereford		£45 / £55
1977	1,138	Westminster		£45 / £55
1978	1,178	Carlisle		£40 / £50
1979	1,189	Winchester		£40 / £50
1980	1,198	Worcester		£40 / £50
1981	1,208	Westminster		£40 / £50
1982	1,218	St.David's Cathedral		£40 / £50
1983	1,218	Exeter Cathedral		£40 / £50
1984	1,243	Southwell Minster		£40 / £50
1985	1,248	Ripon Cathedral		£40 / £50
1986	1,378	Chichester Cathedral		£50 / £60
1987	1,390	Ely Cathedral		£50 / £60
1988	1,402	Lichfield Cathedral		£50 / £60
1989	1,353	Birmingham Cathedral	(63p)	£50 / £60
1990	1,523	St. Nicholas Newcastle	(64p)	£50 / £60
1991	1,384	Westminster	(65p)	£50 / £60
1992	1,424	Chester	(66p)	£50 / £60
1993	1,440	Wells Cathedral	(67p)	£50 / £60
1994	1,437	Truro Cathedral	(68p)	£75 / £85
1995	1,466	Coventry Cathedral	(69p)	£75 / £85
1996		Norwich Cathedral	(70p)	£75 / £85
1997		Bradford Cathedral	(71p)	£80 / £95
1998		Portsnouth Cathedral	(72p)	£80 / £95
1999		Bristol Cathedral	(73p)	£80 / £95
2000		Lincoln Cathedral	(74p)	
2001	12th April	Westminster	(75p)	
2002	28th May	Canterbury Cathedral	(76p)	
2003	....			
2004	....			

	1d	2d	3d	4d		1d	2d	3d	4d
		M A U N D Y			**O D D M E N T S**	(Virtually Mintlike)			
1822	£10	£22	£25	£30	1898	--	--	--	£7
1822	3d has small head				1900	--	£4	--	--
1823	£10	--	--	--	1902	--'	£4	£12	--
1830	£10	--	--	--	1903	£9	£10	--	---
1835	£10	--	--	--	1904	£9	£5	£9	£6
1836	£9	--	--	--	1905	£9	£9	£9	---
1850	£6	--	--	£6	1911	--	--	--	£9
1870	£5	--	--	--	1912	£12	£9	£12	£12
1872	£6	--	--	--	1917	£12	£12	--	---
1880	£5	--	--	--	1941	£12	---	--	---
1888	£5	--	--	--	1951	---	---	£15	---
1890	--	--	--	£6	1953	£60	£50	£50	£50
1891	--	£5	--	--					
1896	--	£4	--	£6					

SHILLINGS

Date	Mintage/etc	(ESC)	Fair/Fine	V.F.	E.F.	abt Unc/FDC
GEORGE IV						**SILVER 23mm**
LAUREATE HEAD · GARNISHED SHIELD · DATE BELOW HEAD						
1820	Pattern				(1986)	£2,012
1821	2,463,120		£6/£9	£25	£75	£140/£180
1821	A proof		---	---	---	£400/£600
LAUREATE HEAD · GARTERED SHIELD · DATE BELOW HEAD						
1823	693,000		£15	£50	£125	£225/£350
1823	A proof		---	---	---	£800
1824	4,158,000		£3/£9	£20	£75	£140/£180
1824	A proof		---	---	---	£450
1825	2,459,160	(1253)	£8/£15	£30	£90	£145/£200
1825	A proof		---	---	---	£450
1825	5 struck over 3		---	---	---	----
BARE HEAD · LION on CROWN · DATE BELOW HEAD						
1825	Included above		£2/£6	£20	£50	£95/£125
1825	A proof		---	---	---	£450
1825	I for 1 in date		---	---	---	£125/£200
1825	A proof struck in Barton's Metal ★				---	£900
1826	6,351,840	(1257)	£2/£4	£8	£30	£65/£95
1826	A proof	(1258)		---	£95	FDC £200
1826	6 struck over a 2nd 2		---	£20	£60	£120/£180
1827	574,200		£8/£15	£45	£100	£250/£300
1829	879,120		£8/£15	£30	£90	£180/£250

★ Barton's Metal is a 'sandwich' of 1 slice of copper between 2 slices of gold

46 SHILLINGS

WILLIAM IV

W.W. in script on truncation of neck — SILVER 23mm

Date	Mintage/etc	Fair/Fine	V.F.	E.F.	Unc/FDC
1831	Proofs, plain edge, from sets		£135		£300/£400
1831	Proofs, grained (milled) edge		---		£700
1834	3,223,440	£5/£9	£20	£70	£120/£185
1834	A proof with flat topped '3' (1988)			"FDC"	£600
1834	W W (block, no stops)				
1835	1,449,360	£6/£10	£30	£90	£175/£225
1836	3,567,960	£6/£10	£30	£90	£175/£225
1837	479,160	£10	£30	£100	£160/£250
1837	A proof (1984 "abt.FDC" £300)				(1997 "abt.FDC" £700)

VICTORIA

FIRST YOUNG HEAD — SILVER 23mm

Date	Mintage/etc	Fair/Fine	V.F.	E.F.	Unc/FDC
1838 W.W.	1,956,240	£6	£16	£60	£120/£150
1838 W.W.	Proofs	--	---	---	£400/£600
1839 W.W.	5,666,760	£4	£12	£40	£80/£120
1839 W.W.	Proofs, plain edged		---	---	£250

SECOND YOUNG HEAD

Date	Mintage/etc	Fair/Fine	V.F.	E.F.	Unc/FDC
1839	Proof (with W.W.) from the sets				£350
1839	No W.W. at neck	£2	£12	£45	£90/£150
1839	Proof (no W.W.) grained edge			---	£750
1840	1,639,440	£3/£9	£25	£85	£125/£200
1841	875,160	£3/£9	£25	£85	£125/£200
1842	2,094,840	£9	£12	£40	£80/£120

VICTORIA   SECOND YOUNG HEAD — SILVER 23mm

Date	Mintage/etc	Fair/Fine	V.F.	E.F.	Unc/FDC
1843	1,465,200	£10	· £20	£60	£120/£180
1844	4,466,880	£9	£15	£50	£100/£150
1845	4,082,760	£9	£14	£35	£70/£100
1846	4,031,280	£9	£14	£35	£70/£100
1848 (*)	1,041,480	£30	£62	£200	£300/ ---
1848	(Mason 2000) "no overstrike nr. EF"				£160
1849	645,480	£9	£15	£50	£95/£150
1850	685,080	£90	£300	£925	£1,500
1850	50 over 46		£400	---	----
1850	50 over 49		---	£1500	/ ---
1851	470,071	£15 / £30	£75	£250	£450/ ---
1852	1,306,574	£8	£15	£50	£95/£140
1853	4,256,188	£7	£14	£45	£90/£120
1853	Proofs from the sets			---	£300/£500
1854	552,414	£40	£125	£350	£700/£950
1854/1		£125	£450	£1000	---/----
1855	1,368,499	£2/£6	£15	£45	£85/£115
1856	3,168,000	£2/£6	£15	£45	£85/£115
1857	2,562,120	£2/£6	£15	£45	£85/£115
1857	REG F: 9: (error inverted G)			£450	---/----
1858	3,108,600	£6	£15	£45	£85/£125
1858/8	(Mason 1994) "Unrecorded over-date abt. EF" £65				

(*) 1848 all second 8 struck over 6

Date	Mintage	Fair/Fine	V.F.	E.F.	Unc/abtFDC
VICTORIA		**SECOND YOUNG HEAD**			**SILVER 23mm**
1859	4,561,920	£6	£15	£45	£85/£125
1860	1,671,120	£8	£20	£60	£110/£160
1861	1,382,040	£8	£20	£60	£110/£160
1861	1 over tilted 1		(1988 near E.F. £45)		---
1861	1 over tilted 1		(Cooke 1998) "BU deep toning" £135		
1862	954,360	£10	£40	£90	£150/£225
1863	859,320	£20	£40	£100	£200/£295
1863/1		£50	£125	£250	---/----

THE FOLLOWING HAVE A DIE NUMBER (above date)

Date	Mintage	Fair/Fine	V.F.	E.F.	Unc/abtFDC
1864	4,518,360	£2/£6	£15	£45	£85/£120
1865	5,619,240	£2/£6	£15	£45	£85/£120
----	(ESC 1398) Undated pattern (Seaby 1988) "abt.FDC" £650				
1866	4,989,600	£6	£15	£45	£80/£125
1866	(Weeks 1994) "Gem, BU/FDC proof-like"				£125
1866	BBITANNIAR error (Coin Mkt. Values 1995)			"EF"	£350
1867	2,166,120	£6	£15	£45	£80/£125
1867	Proof without Die No. grained edge				£500/----
1867	Proof without Die No. plain edge				£1000/----

A specialist collection: all possible die numbers of a single date !

THIRD HEAD, larger, lower relief

Date	Mintage	Fair/Fine	V.F.	E.F.	Unc/abtFDC
1867	Included above	£20	£60	£200	£350/----
1868	3,330,360	£6	£15	£45	£90/£125
1869	736,560	£9	£18	£50	£100/£150
1870	1,467,471	£9	£20	£60	£100/£150
1871	4,910,010	£5	£12	£40	£70/£100
1872	8,897,781	£5	£12	£35	£65/ £95
1873	6,489,598	£5	£12	£40	£70/£100
1874	5,503,747	£5	£12	£40	£70/£100
1874	With crosslet 4	--	£12	£40	£70/£100
1875	4,353,983	£5	£10	£30	£60/ £80
1876	1,057,487	£5	£12	£40	£90/£125
1877	2,980,703	£5	£10	£30	£50/ £75
1877	Believed to exist without Die Number				---/----
1878	3,127,131	£5	£12	£35	£65/ £95
1879	3,611,507	£20	£50	£125	£225/£325
1879	6 over 8 (Die 13)	(Numis. Circ.)			May, 1983

Young Head DIE NUMBER DISCONTINUED

Reverse: CROWNED ONE SHILLING IN WREATH · SILVER 23mm

Date	Mintage	Fair/Fine	V.F.	E.F.	Unc/abtFDC
1879	Fourth Head (Inc. page 33)	£6	£12	£45	£90/---
1880	4,842,786	£2/£5	£10	£25	£50/£75
1881	5,255,332	£2/£5	£10	£25	£50/£75
1881	Shorter line below SHILLING		£10	£25	£50/£75
1882	1,611,786	£10	£30	£80	£150/---
1883	7,281,450	£2/£5	£10	£25	£45/£65
1884	3,923,993	£2/£5	£10	£25	£45/£65
1885	3,336,527	£2/£5	£9	£25	£40/£60
1886	2,086,819	£2/£5	£9	£20	£40/£60
1887	4,034,133 Young head	£5	£18	£50	£90/£125

VICTORIA

Date	Mintage	Fair/Fine	V.F.	E.F.	Unc/abt FDC

Jubilee Head   small head to 1889

Reverse: SHIELD IN GARTER · SILVER 23mm

Date	Mintage	Fair/Fine	V.F.	E.F.	Unc/abt FDC
1887	Included page 47	£1	£4	£6	£12/£18
1887	Long tailed 'Q' in 'QUE'			"abt.BU"	£22
1887	1,084 proofs from the sets			- - -	£50/£75
1888	Last 8 over 7	- -	£6	£20	£40/£60
1888	4,526,856	£2	£5	£15	£25/£40
1889	7,039,628	£10/£25	£80	£275	£365/£450
1889	★ Larger head	£3	£6	£20	£40/£60
1890	8,794,042	£2	£6	£20	£40/£60
1891	5,665,348	£2/£4	£8	£25	£40/£60
1892	4,591,622	£2/£4	£6	£25	£40/£60

Proofs exist for other dates but are rarely offered.

Messrs. Seaby's "The English Silver Coinage" lists some 40 patterns.

> 1887 "shuttlecock" varieties : embellishment divides date · 18 ❦ 87
> The device points to a rim tooth = Reverse A   Rare
> The device points between two teeth = Reverse B   Common

Old, Veiled or Widow Head

THREE SHIELDS within GARTER · SILVER 23mm

Date	Mintage	Fair/Fine	V.F.	E.F.	Unc/abt FDC
1893	7,039,074	£3	£6	£10	£25/£45
1893	Obv. small letters		£12	£20	£40/£60
1893	(noted 1998)		- -	- - -	FDC £72
1893	1,312 proofs from the sets				£45/£65
1894	5,953,152	£3	£6	£16	£35/£50
1895	8,880,651	£1/£4	£10	£20	£30/£45
1896	9,264,551	£1/£3	£6	£16	£25/£40
1897	6,270,364	£1/£3	£6	£20	£40/£60
1898	9,768,703	£1/£3	£6	£20	£40/£60
1899	10,965,382	£3	£6	£16	£20/£32
1900	10,937,590	£3	£6	£12	£20/£35
1901	3,426,294	£3/£5	£9	£18	£30/£45

EDWARD VII

Reverse: LION on CROWN · SILVER 23mm

Date	Mintage	Fair/Fine	V.F.	E.F.	Unc/abt FDC
1902	7,809,481	£2	£5	£20	£30/£50
1902	15,123	Proofs matt finish		- - -	£30/£40
1903	2,061,823	£4	£15	£50	£95/£180
1904	2,040,161	£5	£20	£60	£120/£175
1905 (★)	488,390	£18/£40	£100	£300	£600/- - -
1905	(noted 2001)	"abt.E.F."		£375	- - - -/- - -
1906	10,791,025	£3	£6	£20	£30/£50
1907	14,083,418	£3	£6	£18	£30/£50
1908	3,806,969	£3	£12	£60	£95/£175
1909	5,664,982	£3	£12	£60	£95/£175
1910	26,547,236	£2	£8	£20	£40/£60

(★)   Such a rarity attracts the forger !!

Date	Mintage	Fair/Fine	V.F.	E.F.	Unc/abt.
GEORGE V		LION-on-CROWN · Date Divided · Inner Circle			
1911	20,065,901	£2	£6	£12	£22/£32
1911	6,007 proofs	- - -	- - -		£28/£35
1911	(noted 2002) proof		- - -	"FDC"	£50
1912	15,594,009	£2	£6	£20	£30/£50
1913	9,011,509	£2	£6	£26	£45/£70
1913	(noted 1997)	- - -	- -	"BU"	- - -/£60
1913	(noted 1997)	- - -	- -	"FDC"	- - -/£75
1914	23,415,843	£1	£5	£10	£25/£35
1915	39,279,024	- - -	£3	£6	£12/£20
1916	35,862,015	- - -	£3	£6	£12/£20
1917	22,202,608	- - -	£3	£8	£15/£25
1918	34,915,934	- - -	£3	£6	£12/£20
1919	10,823,824	£3	£8	£20	£45/£55

Obverse 1 = above B.M. the neck is hollow.

Reverse A = GEORGIVS (I points *BETWEEN* beads)

Obverse 2 = above B.M. the neck is flat.

Reverse B = GEORGIVS (I points *TO* a bead)

1911 Varieties: 1 + A; 1 + B; 2 + A; 2 + B.

1912 Varieties: IMP closely spaced; I M P widely spaced.

				SILVER REDUCED to .500	
1920	22,825,142	£2	£5	£15	£30/£40
1921	22,648,763	£2	£6	£18	£30/£50
1921	(noted 2002) "BU Gem rare,"				- - -/£65
1922	27,215,738	£2	£4	£12	£30/£45
1923	14,575,243	£1	£3	£10	£25/£35
1923	Trial Piece in nickel		- - -	£200	£400
1924	Trial in nickel	- - -	- - -	£200	£400
1924	9,250,095	£1	£5	£15	£20/£35
1925	A pattern in nickel		- - -	- - -	- - -/- - -
1925	(noted 1990) Lead pattern · worded MODEL			£175	"nr.VF"
1925	5,418,764	£2	£6	£25	£50/£70
1925	(noted 1999)	- -	- -	"Choice BU"	£70
1926	22,516,453	£1	£4	£12	£20/£36
1926	Modified Effigy	£1	£3	£9	£20/£32
1927	9,262,344	£1	£5	£15	£25/£35
	1920 Varieties: Obverse 1; Obverse 2.				
	LION-on-CROWN · DATE at RIGHT · No inner circle				
1927	NEW DESIGN	£1	£2	£9	£18/£25
1927	15,000 proofs		- - -	- - -	£20/£30
1928	18,136,778	- - -	£1	£5	£10/£15
1929	19,343,006	- - -	£1	£5	£10/£15
1930	3,137,092	£2	£6	£20	£40/£60
1931	6,993,926	£1	£2	£6	£12/£20
1932	12,168,101	£1	£2	£5	£10/£15
1933	11,511,624	- - -	£2	£6	£12/£20
1934	6,138,463	£1	£2	£10	£20/£30
1935	9,183,462	- - -	£1	£5	£10/£15
1936	11,910,613	- - -	£1	£5	£10/£15

SHILLINGS

Date	Mintage	Fine	V.F.	E.F.	Unc/abtFDC

EDWARD VIII (Duke of Windsor)

Reverse: LION SEJANT GUARDANT

| 1936 | few "Scottish" no "English" "Guesstimate" | | | | £18,000 |
| 1937 | COAT of ARMS silver proof by Maklouf | | | "FDC" | £22 |

GEORGE VI   50% SILVER/50% ALLOY until 1947

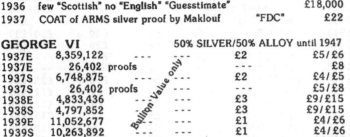

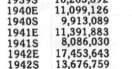

Date	Mintage	Fine	V.F.	E.F.	Unc/abtFDC
1937E	8,359,122	---	---	£2	£5/£6
1937E	26,402 proofs			---	£8
1937S	6,748,875	---	---	£2	£4/£5
1937S	26,402 proofs		---	---	£5/£8
1938E	4,833,436	---	---	£3	£9/£15
1938S	4,797,852		---	£3	£9/£15
1939E	11,052,677	---	---	£1	£4/£6
1939S	10,263,892	---	---	£1	£4/£6
1940E	11,099,126	---	---	£1	£4/£6
1940S	9,913,089	---	---	£1	£4/£6
1941E	11,391,883	---	---	£1	£4/£6
1941S	8,086,030	---	---	£2	£5/£7
1942E	17,453,643	---	---	£1	£3/£4
1942S	13,676,759	---	---	£1	£3/£6
1943E	11,404,213	---	---	£1	£3/£5
1943S	9,824,214	---	---	£1	£3/£5
1944E	11,586,752	---	---	£1	£3/£4
1944S	10,990,167	---	---	£1	£3/£5
1945E	15,143,404	---	---	60p	£2/£4
1945S	15,106,270	---	---	75p	£2/£4
1946E	18,663,797		---	75p	£2/£3
1946E	Pattern, proof, or trial in cupro-nickel				£750
1946E	16,381,501	---	---	£1	£3/£4
1947E	12,120,611	---	---	£1	£4/£6
1947S	12,282,223	---	---	£1	£4/£6
1948E	45,576,923	---	---	£1	£3/£5
1948S	45,351,937	---	---	£1	£3/£5
1949E	19,328,405	---	---	£1	£5/£7
1949S	21,243,074	---	---	£2	£6/£9
1950E	19,243,872	---	---	£5	£10/£15
1950E	17,513 proofs	---	---	F.D.C.	£10
1950S	14,299,601	---	---	£5	£10/£15
1950S	17,513 proofs	---	---	F.D.C.	£10
1951E	9,956,930	---	---	£1	£5/£7
1951E	20,000 proofs	---	---	F.D.C.	£7
1951S	10,961,174	---	---	£2	£5/£7
1951S	20,000 proofs	---	---	F.D.C.	£8
1952E	1 known outside of the Rotal Collection				-----
1952E	(Coincraft 1997) This may be a proof of that date				£8,000

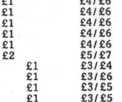

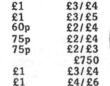

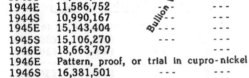

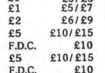

(1)

(2)

Pointings:
1946E   Reverse A ̇IND   Reverse B ̈IND
Reverse A 'I' points TO a rim bead. Reverse B the 'I' points BETWEEN two beads

---

Suffix E = English; S = Scottish. In 1937 these coins were struck with either English or with Scottish symbols and were circulated, generally, throughout the United Kingdom. The practice continued until 1966 and repeated for 1970.

(3)

(4)

Date	Mintage	Fine	V.F.	E.F.	Unc/from/to
ELIZABETH II				CUPRO-NICKEL	23mm
1953E	41,942,894	- - -	- - -	30p	60p/£1
1953	Head both sides, undated but BRITT.OMN				£300
1953E	40,000 proofs		- - -	F.D.C.	£6
1953S	20,663,528	- - -	- - -	30p	£1/£2
1953S	40,000 proofs		- - -	F.D.C.	£6
	BRITT.OMN discontinued				
1954E	30,262,032	- - -	- - -	45p	£2/ £4
1954S	26,771,735	- - -	- - -	36p	£2/ £4
1955E	45,259,908	- - -	- - -	36p	£2/ £4
1955S	27,950,906	- - -	- - -	50p	£3/ £6
1956E	44,907,008	- - -	- - -	£2	£6/£12
1956S	42,853,637	- - -	- - -	£2	£6/£12
1957E	42,774,217	- - -	- - -	25p	£2/ £4
1957E	V.I.P proof	- - -	- - -	F.D.C.	£200
1957S	17,959,988	- - -	- - -	£3	£12/£18
1957S	V.I.P. proof	- - -	- - -	F.D.C.	£200
1958E	14,392,305	- - -	- - -	£3	£10/£15
1958E	V.I.P. proof	- - -	- - -	(noted 2001)	£275
1958S	40,822,557	- - -	- - -	25p	£1/ £2
1959E	19,442,778	- - -	- - -	25p	£1/ £2
1959S	1,012,988	15p	50p	£3	£12/£18
1960E	27,027,914	- - -	- - -	25p	£1/ £2
1960S	14,376,932	- - -	- - -	25p	£1/ £2
1961E	39,816,907	- - -	- - -	15p	£1/ £2
1961E	A proof	(offered 1998)		"FDC"	£165
1961S	2,762,558	- - -	10p	75p	£3/ £6
1961S	A proof	(offered 1984)		"FDC"	200
1962E	36,704,379	- - -	- - -	- - -	50p/£1
1962S	18,967,310	- - -	- - -	- - -	50p/£1
1963E	44,714,000	- - -	- - -	- - -	50p/£1
1963S	32,300,000	- - -	- - -	- - -	20p/40p
1964E	8,590,900	- - -	- - -	- - -	30p/50p
1964S	5,239,100	- - -	- - -	- - -	50p/75p
1965E	9,218,000	- - -	- - -	- - -	30p/60p
1965S	2,774,000	- - -	- - -	- - -	50p/£1
1966E	15,005,000	includes 3,000 minted in 1967			45p/£1
1966S	15,607,000	includes 3,000 minted in 1967			45p/£1
1966S	Head/Tail reversed	↑↓		- - -	£30/£50
1968	Decimal equivalent FIVE NEW PENCE introduced				
1970E	750,476 proofs LAST STERLING set				£1.50/£3
1970S	750,476 proofs LAST STERLING set				£1.50/£3

Some Heraldic terms:
STATANT GUARDANT - see pic (1) 1937 Page 50
SEJANT GUARDANT - sideways, facing; pic (2) 1937 Page 50
RAMPANT - such as lion rampant, see pic (3) 1953.
PASSANT GUARDANT - see the three leopards pic (4) 1953.
Passant guardant is sometimes described as couchant (lying down),
but the raised paw indicates otherwise. The three leopards are still
referred to as such on old coinage, but on modern strikings are likely
to be referred to as three lions.

FLORINS · (Two Shillings)

VICTORIA

SILVER 28mm

GODLESS (having no DEI GRATIA)

		Fine	V.F.	E.F.	Unc/abtFDC
1848	(ESC799) Plain edge proof	---	---		£1600
1848	As above but with grained (milled) edge				£500/£600
1848	(ESC886) Plain edge pattern (2001nr. FDC)				£495
1849	413,830 'Godless'	£12	£25	£75	£125/£165

GOTHIC · date appears in Roman · third column · 30mm.

		Fine	V.F.	E.F.	Unc/abtFDC
1851	1,540 mbcccli	£2000		(report 1995)	----/----
1852	1,014,552 mbccclii	£12	£30	£90	£150/£200
1852	ii struck over i	(Messrs. Weeks 1993)		£95	"abtEF"
1853 ★	3,919,950 mbcccliii	£10	£40	£95	£175/£300
1853	Proof	----	----	----	£800/£1000
1854	550,413 mbccclib	£200	£500	£1800	----/----
1855	831,017 mbccclb	£10	£25	£100	£175/£250
1856 ★	2,201,760 mbccclbi	£10	£26	£110	£200/£275
1857	1,671,120 mbccclbii	£10	£25	£100	£150/£250
1857	Proof (ESC815)	----	----	----	£875
1858 +	2,239,380 mbccclbiii	£10	£25	£100	£150/£200
1858	(Seaby 1989) "no stop after date"			£110	"EF/gdEF"
1859 +	2,568,060 mbccclbix	£10	£25	£100	£150/£200
1860	1,475,100 mbccclx	£10	£30	£125	£200/£300
1862	594,000 mbccclxii	£20	£100	£300	£400/£600
1863	938,520 mbccclxiii	£40	£150	£500	£950/£1400
1864	1,861,200 mbccclxib	£10	£25	£100	£175/£250
1865 !	1,580,044 mbccclxb	£10	£30	£105	£175/£225
1865 !	(Mason 1994)			"abt.UNC"	£110/----
1866 !	914,760 mbccclxbi	£10	£30	£125	£180/£250
1867	423,720 mbccclxbii	£15	£60	£200	£340/£450
1868	896,940 mbccclxbiii	£10	£30	£125	£180/£250
1869	297,000 mbccclxix	£10	£25	£100	£150/£200
1870	1,080,648 mbccclxx	£10	£25	£100	£150/£200
1871	3,425,605 mbccclxxi	£10	£25	£100	£150/£200
1872	7,199,690 mbccclxxii	£10	£25	£80	£120/£175
1873	5,921,839 mbccclxxiii	£10	£25	£80	£140/£200

```
★ Have varieties with no stop after date.  Rarity R2
+ Have varieties with no stop after date.  Rarity R
! With  colon  after date:  1865  R3;  1866  R2
1867 brit: is normal;      proofs/patterns have britt;
R = rare;    R2 = very rare;    Seaby/Rayner scale.
```

VICTORIA   GOTHIC · date appears in Roman · third column · 30mm.

			Fine	V.F.	E.F.	Unc/abtFDC
1874	1,642,630	m𝖉𝖈𝖈𝖈𝖑𝖝𝖝𝖎𝖇	£10	£25	£80	£140/£200
1874	𝖎𝖇 struck over 𝖎𝖎𝖎		£25	£60	(noted	1999)
1875	1,117,030	m𝖉𝖈𝖈𝖈𝖑𝖝𝖝𝖇	£10	£30	£100	£150/£200
1876	580,034	m𝖉𝖈𝖈𝖈𝖑𝖝𝖝𝖇𝖎	£10	£30	£100	£165/ - - - -
1877	682,292	m𝖉𝖈𝖈𝖈𝖑𝖝𝖝𝖇𝖎𝖎	£10	£30	£100	£165/ - - - -
1877	No WW	(48 arcs)	£15	£60	£200	- - - - / - - - -
1877	No WW	(42 arcs)	£12	£50	£120	£190/ - - - -
1878	1,786,680	m𝖉𝖈𝖈𝖈𝖑𝖝𝖝𝖇𝖎𝖎𝖎	£10	£25	£100	£150/£200
1879	1,512,247	m𝖉𝖈𝖈𝖈𝖑𝖝𝖝𝖎𝖝 :	£10	£25	£100	£150/£200
Die No.	48 arcs WW	(ESC 849B)	£30	£80	- - - -	- - - - / - - - -
No Die No.	42 arcs	(ESC 850)	£20	£70	(no WW)	- - - - / - - - -
No Die No.	48 arcs	(ESC 851)	£10	£30	£120	£165/£250
No WW	38 arcs	(ESC 852)	£10	£25	£100	£150/£200
1880	Younger portrait		extremely rare		- - - -	- - - - / - - - -
1880	2,167,170	m𝖉𝖈𝖈𝖈𝖑𝖝𝖝𝖝	£9	£24	£90	£150/£225
1880	(noted 1999)		"VF+"	£65	- - - -	- - - - / - - - -
1881	2,570,337	m𝖉𝖈𝖈𝖈𝖑𝖝𝖝𝖝𝖎	£5	£25	£75	£150/£225
1881	broken die	m𝖉𝖈𝖈𝖈𝖑𝖝𝖝𝖗𝖎	£10	£45	£95	£160/£250
1883	3,555,667	m𝖉𝖈𝖈𝖈𝖑𝖝𝖝𝖝𝖎𝖎𝖎	£5	£25	£95	£160/£250
1884	1,447,379	m𝖉𝖈𝖈𝖈𝖑𝖝𝖝𝖝𝖎𝖇	£5	£25	£95	£160/£250
1885	1,758,210	m𝖉𝖈𝖈𝖈𝖑𝖝𝖝𝖝𝖇	£7	£28	£100	£165/£260
1886	591,773	m𝖉𝖈𝖈𝖈𝖑𝖝𝖝𝖝𝖇𝖎	£5	£25	£95	£160/£250
1887	1,776,903	m𝖉𝖈𝖈𝖈𝖑𝖝𝖝𝖝𝖇𝖎𝖎	£8	£30	£130	£225/£300

Those above and on page 52 are inscribed 𝖔𝖓𝖊 𝖙𝖊𝖓𝖙𝖍 𝖔𝖋 𝖆 𝖕𝖔𝖚𝖓𝖉
Proofs exist for many dates; they are rare and rarely offered

Jubilee Head (see page 40)   29.5mm

1887	Included above	£2	£5	£9	£15/£25
1887	1,084 Jubilee Head proofs			£40	£80/£125
1888	1,541,540	£2	£4	£15	£30/£50
1889	2,973,561	£2/£3	£5	£18	£35/£60
1890	1,684,737	£4	£15	£60	£85/£150
1891	836,438	£10	£40	£100	£150/£225
1892	283,401	£12	£40	£95	£140/£200

Old, Veiled or Widow Head (see page 40)   28.5mm

1893	1,666,103	£2	£6	£25	£50/£75
1893	1,312 proofs		- - -	- - -	- - -/£125
1894	1,952,842	£3	£8	£30	£50/£75
1895	2,182,968	£3	£8	£28	£45/£70
1896	2,944,416	£3	£8	£28	£45/£70
1897	1,699,921	£2/£3	£6	£30	£45/£70
1898	3,061,343	£3	£6	£25	£45/£70
1899	3,966,953	£2	£5	£25	£40/£60
1900	5,528,630	£2	£5	£25	£40/£60
1901	2,648,870	£2	£6	£30	£45/£70

Date	Mintage	Fair/Fine	V.F.	E.F.	Unc/abtFDC

EDWARD VII STANDING BRITANNIA · SILVER 28.5mm

Date	Mintage	Fair/Fine	V.F.	E.F.	Unc/abtFDC
1902	2,189,575	£5	£9	£25	£45/£65
1902	(noted 1999)	--	"BU, Gem"		£60
1902	15,123 matt finished proofs				£40/£50
1903	1,995,298	£5	£25	£55	£80/£120
1904	2,769,932	£10	£50	£150	£200/£325
1905	1,187,596	£30	£80	£250	£400/£500
1905	(noted 2000)		"gd. E.F."		£240 --
1906	6,910,128	£5	£10	£50	£150/£200
1907	5,947,895·	£5	£12	£70	£90/£140
1908	3,280,010	£6	£18	£90	£140/£200
1909	3,482,289	£6	£18	£90	£140/£200
1909	(noted 2001)	---	"Mint State"		£300
1910	5,650,713	£5	£10	£50	£75/ £95

GEORGE V SHIELDS/SCEPTRES in Quarters · 28.5mm

1911	5,951,284	£2	£5	£25	£40/£60
1911	6,007 proofs	---		£30	£40/£60
1912	8,571,731	£4	£8	£40	£60/£85
1913	4,545,278	£5	£15	£45	£80/£100
1914	21,252,701	£2	£6	£12	£20/£30
1915	12,367,939	£2	£3	£12	£24/£36
1916	21,064,337	£2	£6	£20	£40/£60
1917	11,181,617	£2	£6	£20	£30/£50
1918	29,211,792	£2	£6	£10	£20/£30
1919	9,469,292	£2	£6	£15	£30/£45

GEORGE V SHIELDS/SCEPTRES in Quarters · 28.5mm
FROM 1920 SILVER REDUCED TO 50%

1920	15,387,833	£2	£7	£20	£50/ £60
1921	34,863,895	£3	£7	£15	£30/ £45
1922	23,861,044	£3	£7	£15	£30/ £45
1923	21,546,533	£3	£7	£15	£28/ £40
1924	4,582,372	£3	£9	£25	£50/ £75
1925	1,404,136	£10	£30	£90	£135/£210
1925	Uniface lead pattern : (Seaby 1990) "vf+"				£225
1926	5,125,410	£3	£9	£25	£60/£75
1927	15,000 proofs of new design				£40/£65
1928	11,087,186	£2	£4	£8	£12/£18
1929	16,397,279	£2	£4	£7	£15/£20
1929	(noted 2001)	---	"FDC"		£25
1930	5,753,568	£2	£4	£8	£12/£18
1931	6,556,331	£2	£4	£7	£10/£18

1932	717,041	£10	£20	£80	£125/£225
1933	8,685,303	£2	£4	£8	£16/£30
1934	none	---	---	---	---/---
1935	7,540,546	£1	£3	£6	£12/£18
1936	9,897,448	£1	£2	£4	£12/£18

1911	Two obverses (see page 9)
1914	Large rim teeth and small rim teeth
1920	BRITT and BRITT (rim pointings)

FLORINS (Two Shillings) 55

Date	Mintage	Fine	V.F.	E.F.	abt. Unc/FDC

EDWARD VIII   as GEORGE VI but monogram ER

| 1937 | | "Guesstimate" | | £12,000/£15,000 |
| 1937 | Pattern in sterling silver by Maklouf | | | FDC £25 |

GEORGE VI

50/50 silver/alloy until 1947

Date	Mintage	Fine	V.F.	E.F.	abt. Unc/FDC
1937	13,006,781	50p	£2	£3	£4/£6
1937	26,402 proofs	- - -	- - -		£8/£10
1938	7,909,388	50p	£3	£8	£16/£20
1939	20,850,607	50p	£2	£4	£6/£8
1939	Proof	- - -	(Spinks 1986)		/£165
1940	18,700,338	50p	£2	£3	£4/£5
1941	24,451,079	50p	£2	£3	£4/£5
1942	39,895,243	50p	£2	£3	£4/£5
1943	26,711,987	50p	£2	£3	£4/£5
1944	27,560,005	50p	£1	£3	£4/£5
1945	25,858,049	50p	£1	£2	£3/£4
1946	22,910,085	50p	£1	£2	£4/£5

CUPRO-NICKEL

Date	Mintage	Fine	V.F.	E.F.	abt. Unc/FDC
1946	Trial Piece, new coinage, cupro-nickel,				- - / - - -
1947	22,910,085	- - -	- - -	£2	£5/£8
1948	67,553,636	- - -	- - -	£1	£2/£4
1949	28,614,939	- - -	- - -	£2	£8/£12
1949	Proof	- - -	- - -	- - -	£160/- - -
1950	24,357,490	- - -	- - -	£2	£8/£15
1950	17,513 proofs			FDC	£15
1951	27,411,747	- - -	- - -	£3	£6/£9
1951	20,000 proofs		- - -	FDC	£10

ELIZABETH II

Date	Mintage	Fine	V.F.	E.F.	abt. Unc/FDC
1953	11,958,710	- - -	- - -	£1	£2/£4
1953	40,000 proofs		- - -	- - -	£4/£6

BRITT: OMN: not now included in legend

(Glendinings 2000)		Rev. TRIAL DIE		£460
1954	13,085,422	- - -	- - -	£5	£25/£35
1955	25,887,253	- - -	- - -	£2	£3/£5
1956	47,824,500	- - -	- - -	£2	£3/£5
1957	33,071,282	- - -	- - -	£4	£20/£30
1957	(noted '98 and '99) "V.I.P. proof FDC"				£250
1958	9,564,580	- - -	- - -	£2	£6/£12
1958	(noted '97 and '99) "V.I.P. proof FDC"				£250
1959	14,080,319	- - -	- - -	£5	£10/£15
1960	13,831,782	- - -	- - -	£1	£2/£3
1961	37,735,315	- - -	- - -	£1	£2/£3
1961	(noted 1999)		"V.I.P. proof FDC"		£230
1962	35,147,903	- - -	- - -	50p	£1/£3
1963	25,562,000	- - -	- - -	50p	£1/£3
1964	16,539,000	- - -	- - -	50p	£1/£3
1965	48,163,000	- - -	- - -	50p	£1/£2
1966	84,041,000	- - -	- - -	50p	£1/£2
1967	22,152,000	- - -	- - -	50p	£1/£2
1967	Two tails: reverse both sides			£75	£95/£125
1968	17,566,000 dated 1967.		Decimals introduced.		
1970	750,476 proofs Last Sterling set		- - -		£2/£3

Continued on page 66 under DECIMAL COINAGE

HALF CROWNS
Silver 32 mm

Date   Mintage

GEORGE IV

Date	Mintage	Fine	V.F.	E.F.	Unc/abtFDC
1820	Garnished Shield	£9	£30	£95	£180/£275
1821	1,435,104 Rev.1	£12	£32	£95	£180/£290
1821	(★) Rev.2	£15	£60	£300	£400/ - - - -
1821	Proof	- - -	- - -	£300	£600/£950
1822	Proof (only 2 known)		(1993)	"FDC"	£3,650
1823	2,003,760	£225	£650	£1800	£3,000
1823	Shield in Garter	£9	£35	£120	£250/£375
1823	Pattern	(ESC 652)	(1991)	"FDC"	£4,800
1824	465,696 ?	£14	£60	£180	£260/£350
1824	Bare Head	£500	£750	£2650	- - - - / - - - -
1825	2,258,784	£10	£30	£90	£160/£200
1825	Proofs	(ESC 643; and 644)			/£850
1825	Proof (ESC 645) in Barton's Metal : a 'sandwich' of one slice of copper and two thin slices of gold. (1984) £1,500				
1826	2,189,088	£9	£35	£120	£200/£325
1826	Proofs from the sets		- - -	£150	- - - - /£700
1828	49,890 ?	£12	£50	£120	£200/£325
1829	508,464	£12	£50	£180	£260/£350

Proofs except 1828 and 1829; patterns 1820/22/23/24
Pattern "Binfield" (ESC 655) (1991) " abt.Unc."   £395/ - - - -

(★) 1821 Rev.2 subtle differences, e.g. examine shamrock stems

WILLIAM IV

Date	Mintage	Fine	V.F.	E.F.	Unc/abtFDC
1831	Currency (Coincraft Cat. 1997) £600 "Fine"				- - - - / - - - -
1831	Proofs from the sets		(noted 2001)		£600
1834	993,168 WW	£15	£60	£240	£400/£650
1834	Proof WW	- - -	- - -	- - -	£950/£1200
1834	𝒲 𝒲 in script	£7	£30	£110	£200/£290
1834	Proof 𝒲 𝒲	- - -	- - -	- - -	£950/£1200
1834	Proof 𝒲 𝒲 plain edged	- - -	- - -	- - -	£2000/£3000
1835	281,952	£12	£50	ˉ£150	£300/£450
1836	1,588,752	£6	£25	£110	£200/£300
1836	6 struck over 5	£12	£50	£150	£250/£325
1837	150,526	£12	£50	£150	£250/£360

VICTORIA   Young Head

Date		Fine	V.F.	E.F.	Unc/abtFDC
1839a	Raised WW		£400	£800	£3000
1839a	Proof with grained (milled) edge				- - - - /£2500
1839a	Proof with plain edge, from the sets				- - - - / £600
1839a	(noted 1998) "virtually FDC · pink/blue tones"				£695
1839b	Proof with two ornamented hair fillets				- - - - /£1500
1839c	Proof with two plain hair fillets				- - - - /£3500
1839d	Currency,		£350	£750	£2000	£3000/ - - - -
1839d	Proof, grained (milled) edge				- - -	- - - - /£3000
1839d	Plain edge proofs, from the sets				- - -	- - - - /£4500
1840	386,496		£25	£80	£200	£300/£450
1841	42,768		£250	£500	£1500	£2200/ - - - -
1842	486,288		£20	£50	£160	£250/£375
1843	454,608		£55	£140	£550	£650/£900

> (a) has one plain, one ornamented hair fillet;
> WW, on neck, is raised
> (b) has two ornamental hair fillets: WW raised
> (c) has two plain hair fillets; WW raised
> (d) has two plain hair fillets;
> WW incuse (struck in)

Date	Mintage	Fine	V.F.	E.F.	Unc./abt FDC
VICTORIA	Young Head				SILVER 32 mm
1844	1,999,008	£12	£40	£125	£230/£300
1845	2,231,856	£10	£35	£100	£175/£275
1846	1,539,668	£15	£45	£120	£200/£300
1846	8 struck over 1	£16	£50	£160	£300/£375
1846	8 struck over 7	£60	£200	£600	£1200/----
1848	367,488 2nd 8/6	£30	£120	£360	£475/£650
1849	261,360 large date	£15	£50	£200	£300/£400
1849	Smaller date	£30	£100	£300	£750/£950
1850	484,613	£15	£55	£200	£350/£450
1853	Proofs from the sets (ESC 687)			---	£1,500
1862	Proofs (ESC 688) and (ESC 689)			---	£2,500
1864	Proof only, for the Albert Memorial			---	£3,000
1874	2,188,599	£10	£25	£80	£160/£225
1875	1,113,483	£10	£25	£75	£145/----
1876	633,221	£12	£30	£80	£150/----
1876	6 struck over 5	£18	£40	£125	£200/----
1877	447,059	£12	£30	£65	£100/£150
1878	1,466,232	£10	£25	£75	£100/£150
1879	901,356	£16	£30	£100	£140/£220
1879	Proof (Seaby 1990)	(ESC704)		"abt.FDC"	£1100
1880	1,346,350	£12	£28	£70	£110/£160
1881	2,301,495	£10	£25	£60	£100/£150
1882	808,227	£12	£25	£75	£125/£200
1883	2,982,779	£12	£28	£80	£120/£200
1884	1,569,175	£10	£25	£75	£120/£200
1885	1,628,438	£12	£28	£75	£120/£200
1886	891,767	£12	£28	£75	£120/£200
1887	261,747 Young Head	£10	£30	£90	£180/£250

58 HALF CROWNS

VICTORIA

SILVER 32 mm

	Mintage		Fine	V.F.	E.F.	Unc/abtFDC.

Jubilee Head

	Mintage		Fine	V.F.	E.F.	Unc/abtFDC.
1887	1,176,299		£3	£7	£14	£20/£30
1887	1,084	proofs	- - -			£125/£175
1888	1,428,787		£4	£9	£30	£50/£75
1889	4,811,954		£4	£9	£30	£45/£70
1890	3,228,111		£4	£12	£40	£60/£95
1891	2,284,632		£4	£12	£40	£60/£95
1892	1,710,946		£4	£12	£40	£60/£95

Old, Veiled or Widow Head

	Mintage		Fine	V.F.	E.F.	Unc/abtFDC.
1893	1,792,600		£4	£8	£25	£50/£75
1893	1,312	proofs	- - -	- - -		£120
1894	1,524,960		£5	£12	£60	£90/£125
1895	1,772,662		£5	£12	£50	£75/£90
1896	2,148,505		£5	£12	£50	£75/£90
1897	1,678,643		£4	£10	£30	£50/£70
1898	1,870,055		£4	£10	£40	£60/£80
1899	2,863,872		£4	£10	£40	£60/£80
1900	4,479,128		£4	£10	£40	£55/£75
1901	1,516,570		£4	£10	£40	£55/£75

Several patterns, proofs and varieties occur.

EDWARD VII

SILVER 32mm

	Mintage		V.F.	E.F.	Unc/abtFDC.
1902	1,316,008	£8	£16	£40	£80/£95
1902	15,123	matt surfaced proofs			£50/£70
1903	274,840	£45	£120	£375	£500/£800
1904	709,652	£35	£110	£275	£400/£600
1905	166,008	£120	£300	£750	£950/£1300
1905	(Nichols '02)	£140	"Fine"	- - -	- - - -/- - -
1906	2,886,206	£8	£25	£60	£100/£175
1906	(S & B '95)	"nr.UNC, nice tone"			£95
1907	3,693,930	£8	£25	£80	£120/£180
1908	1,758,889	£10	£30	£120	£160/£225
1909	3,051,592	£8	£25	£75	£140/£225
1910	2,557,685	£8	£25	£65	£95/£150

Date	Mintage	Fine	V.F.	E.F.	Unc/abtFDC
GEORGE V				SILVER to 1920 32mm	
1911	2,914,573	£3	£9	£25	£50/£75
1911	6,007 proofs		---		£60/£70
1912	4,700,789	£4	£10	£30	£55/£85
1913	4,090,160	£4	£10	£40	£80/£125
1914	18,333,003	£4	£10	£15	£30/£45
1915	32,433,066	£2	£4	£10	£16/£25
1916	29,530,020	£3	£6	£12	£24/£30
1917	11,172,052	£3	£6	£12	£35/£55
1918	29,079,592	£3	£6	£12	£24/£36
1919	10,266,737	£3	£6	£15	£45/£70

NOW REDUCED TO .500 SILVER

Date	Mintage	Fine	V.F.	E.F.	Unc/abtFDC
1920	17,983,077	£2	£5	£20	£45/£70
1920	Small head, high relief Obv 1/Rev B (2001)			£110	
1921	23,677,889 DEI	£2	£5	£25	£45/£70
1921	DEI	£2	£5	£25	
1922	16,396,774 Rev. A	£6	£20	£35/£50	
	Rev. B	£8	£25	£40/£60	

Rev.A = Narrow groove between crown and shield
Rev.B = Wide groove between crown and shield

Date	Mintage	Fine	V.F.	E.F.	Unc/abtFDC
1923	26,308,526	£2	£6	£12	£24/£35
1924	5,866,294	£2	£6	£25	£50/£75
1925	1,413,461	£8	£15	£125	£245/£295
1926	4,473,516	£2	£5	£30	£60/£90
1926	No colon after OMN		£25	£165	£260/----
1926	Modified Effigy	£2	£6	£30	£65/£85
1927	6,852,872	£2	£5	£15	£30/£45
1927	15,000 proofs, new design		---		£25/£35
1928	18,762,727	£2	£5	£8	£16/£25
1929	17,632,636	£2	£5	£8	£16/£25
1930	809,501	£6	£15	£75	£150/£225
1931	11,264,468	£2	£5	£10	£20/£30
1932	4,793,643	£2	£5	£15	£30/£50
1933	10,311,494	£2	£5	£10	£20/£30
1934	2,422,399	£2	£5	£25	£40/£70
1935	7,022,216	£2	£5	£10	£15/£20
1935	A proof changed hands in 1975 for£160/----				
1936	7,039,423	£2	£5	£9	£14/£20

1928 Rosette: ★ = Rev. A; ★ = Rev. B
1929 Varieties as for 1928

EDWARD VIII *(Duke of Windsor)* ·500 SILVER
1937 Standard bearing ROYAL ARMS (1993) £16,000/£20,000
1937 Sterling Silver ROYAL ARMS by Maklouf FDC £25

Date	Mintage	Fine	V.F.	E.F.	Unc/FDC
GEORGE VI			.500	SILVER	until 1947
1937	9,106,440	£1	£2	£4	£9/£12
1937	26,402 proofs		--	FDC	£10
1938	6,426,478	£1	£2	£6	£18/£24
1938	(noted 1996)	"FDC superb"		--	£25
1939	15,478,635	£1	£2	£3	£5/£8
1940	17,948,439	£1	£2	£3	£5/£8
1941	15,773,984	£1	£2	£3	£5/£8
1942	31,220,090	£1	£2	£3	£5/£8
1943	15,462,875	£1	£2	£3	£6/£10
1944	15,255,165	£1	£2	£3	£5/£8
1945	19,849,242	£1	£2	£3	£5/£8
1946	22,724,873	£1	£2	£3	£5/£8

NOW CUPRO-NICKEL (no silver)

1946	Proof (in cupro-nickel)		--	--	£1,250
1947	21,911,484	--	£1	£2	£5/£7
1948	71,164,703	--	£1	£2	£4/£6
1949 ★	28,272,512	--	£2	£3	£5/£8
1950	28,335,500	--	£1	£2	£8/£12
1950	17,513 proofs	--	--	FDC	£12
1951	9,003,520	--	£1	£3	£6/£9
1951	20,000 proofs	--	--	FDC	£8
1952	1 Sold by "Private Treaty" in 1991				£28,500

★ IND: IMP (Emperor of India) discontinued from 1949

ELIZABETH II   CUPRO-NICKEL 32mm

1953	4,333,214	DEI ..		£1	£3/£5
1953	I points between rim beads DEI		--	£2	£4/£6
1953	40,000 proofs	--	--	FDC	---/£7
1954	11,614,953	--	--	£4	£15/£25
1954	Proof	(1985 £225)		(1999 £325)	
1955	23,628,726	--	--	£1	£4/£6
1956	33,934,909	--	--	£2	£6/£8
1957	34,200,563	--	--	£2	£6/£8
1958	15,745,668	--	--	£3	£12/£20
1959	9,028,844	--	--	£4	£15/£25
1960	19,929,191	--	--	£1	£3/£4
1961	25,887,897	--	--	--	£3/£5
1961	Struck on polished blanks				£4/£6
1962	24,013,312	--	--	--	£2/£4
1963	17,557,600	--	--	--	£2/£4
1964	5,973,600	--	--	£1	£2/£4
1965	9,878,400	--	--	--	£1/£3
1966	13,384,000	--	--	--	70p/£2
1967	18,895,200	--	--	--	60p/£1
1968	14,163,200 but dated 1967 · Total 33,058,400				
1969	Halfcrowns were demonetized	31st December.			
1970	Proofs from the 8-coin set	--			£2/£4

Date	Mintage	Fine	V.F.	E.F.	abt. Unc/FDC
VICTORIA	Jubilee Head				SILVER 36mm
1887	483,347 Roman I	£5	£15	£25	£35/£50
1887	Roman I proof	--	--	---	£95/£150
1887	Arabic 1 in date	£5	£15	£25	£40/£60
1887	Arabic 1 proof	--	--	---	£95/£150
1888	243,340	£6	£20	£35	£70/£95
1888 ★	Inverted 1 for second I	£15	£40	£80	£120/£180
1889	1,185,111	£5	£10	£30	£60/£80
1889 ★	Inverted 1 for second I	£15	£40	£80	£120/£180
1890	782,146	£6	£18	£35	£75/£100
1890	Pattern with reverse worded	DOUBLE FLORIN			---

> ★ 2nd I of VICTORIA appears as I
> J.E.B. at truncation = Designer/Engraver Joseph Boehm
> Now thought to be a broken serif rather than inverted type

GEORGE V
SILVER 36mm

| 1910 | Double Florin in gold | (1986) £5,700 |

1911   Rare   Plain and grained edge patterns (sundry metals)
1911   As picture but DOUBLE FLORIN   (1989 abtFDC £450)
1914   worded: TWELVE GROATS   and in various metals

GEORGE VI
SILVER 36mm

1950   Patterns, grained edge, George and Dragon   ext. rare
1950   As previous but 'FOUR SHILLINGS' struck into the edge

Date	Mintage	(ESC No.)	Fine	V.F.	E.F.	Unc/abtFDC

GEORGE IV LAUREATE HEAD · St. George/Dragon Reverse · Silver 38.61mm

Date	Mintage	(ESC No.)	Fine	V.F.	E.F.	Unc/abtFDC
1820	Pattern	(259)	(Dolphin 1993)		"FDC"	£5000
1821	437,976 SECVNDO		£20	£70	£300	£650/£800
1821	SECVNDO proof		(noted 1999)		£2600	----/----
1821	Error TERTIO proof		(noted 1999)		----	£3800
1822	124,929 SECVNDO		£20	£80	£350	£850/£1200
1822	SECVNDO proof			(noted 1999)		£3600
1822	TERTIO		£20	£70	£320	£650/£900
1822	TERTIO proof		(noted 1986)		----	£2300
1823	Without edge number, proof only				(offers to buy £6000)	

BARE HEAD · Shield Reverse

1825		(255) BARE HEAD pattern	(noted 1996)			£5000
1826		(257) SEPTIMO proof from the sets	(1987)			£3000
1828		(263) Pattern in Germanic style	£500	(1998)		-----

WILLIAM IV

Date	MANTLE design as halfcrown			Proofs and patterns only	
1831	W.W.	(271)		(near FDC, minor defects, Seaby £2750)	
1831	W.W.	(272)	Proof in gold (Coincraft Cat. 1997)	£60000	
1831	W.Wyon	(273)	---	---	£3000	/£5200
1832	Lead Pattern, extreme rarity edge TERTIO			£4000	----
1834	A plain edged proof	---	---	£9000	£11000

VICTORIA YOUNG HEAD Silver 38mm

Date			Fine	V.F.	E.F.	Unc/abtFDC
1837	Incuse Pattern by Bonomi		(Auction 1987)			£2600
1837	Pattern, lead, mirror image	(Spink 1988)	£650			----
1839	Proofs (279) from the sets			£1200		£2250/£3250
1844	94,248 Edge VIII :					
	Star-shaped edge stops	£25	£95	£500	£900/£1800
1844	Proof with star-shaped edge stops		---	----	£4000/£7500
1844	Cinquefoil (five leaves) stops	£25	£95	£500	£900/£1800
1845	159,192 Edge VIII	£25	£95	£550	£1500/£2000
1845	L. Skelhorn reports doubled obverse	£500 offered in 1996			
1846	Pattern (341) by W. Wyon	---	(1980)		/£3000
1847	140,976 Edge XI	£25	£75	£400	£800/£1200
1847	8,000 UNDECIMO proof GOTHIC £250 £450 :	£650	£1300/£1900		
1847	Roy Francis pinpoints Spink-Taisei sale 1988, 1 in gold		£113,000		
1847	Error edge SEPTIMO proof GOTHIC		----	-----/-----
1847	Without edge number (ESC 291)	£750	£1200/£1600		
1853	460 (293) DECIMO SEPTIMO from sets	£2000	£3000/£4000		
1853	as previous (Cooke '98) "light scuffs otherwise FDC"		£3750		
1853	(Whiteaves-Scott '95) "Magnificent Gem FDC"		£4250		
1853	(294) Without edge number	----	£4500/£6000		
1879	Return to Young Head. Offers for this exceed		£15,000		

"Gothic" have the obverse inscribed, at perimeter, mdcccxlvii for 1847 etc.

Date	Mintage		Fine	V.F.	E.F.	Unc/abtFDC

VICTORIA *JUBILEE HEAD* GOLDEN JUBILEE

Reverse: ST. GEORGE and THE DRAGON · SILVER 38.61mm

Date	Mintage		Fine	V.F.	E.F.	Unc/abtFDC
1887	173,581		£10	£20	£35	£55/£75
1887	1,084	proof	- -	- - -	£200	£300/£400
1888	131,899	close date £12		£30	£70	£90/£140
1888		wider date £25		£50	£100	£150/£225
1889	1,807,223		£9	£15	£30	£45/£70
1890	997,862		£10	£20	£40	£80/£120
1891	566,394		£10	£25	£60	£90/£140
1892	451,334		£15	£30	£90	£130/£220

Old, Veiled or Widow Head

Date	Mintage		Fine	V.F.	E.F.	Unc/abtFDC
1893	1,312	LVI	proofs from sets		£150	£250/£360
1893	497,845	LVI	£10	£30	£60	£95/£145
1893		LVII	£15	£50	£100	£165/£250
1894	144,906	LVII	£9	£30	£95	£175/£250
1894		LVIII	£9	£30	£80	£160/£240
1895	252,862	LVIII	£9	£30	£80	£160/£220
1895		LIX	£9	£30	£80	£160/£220
1896	317,599	LIX	£12	£40	£130	£250/£375
1896		LX	£9	£30	£80	£120/£200
1897	262,118	LX	£9	£30	£90	£120/£200
1897		LXI	£10	£30	£60	£120/£200
1898	161,450	LXI	£15	£50	£150	£200/£275
1898		LXII	£9	£30	£90	£120/£180
1899	166,300	LXII	£9	£30	£90	£120/£180
1899		LXIII	£9	£30	£90	£120/£180
1900	353,356	LXIII	£15	£50	£95	£150/£250
1900		LXIV	£15	£50	£100	£175/£300

EDWARD VII   Reverse: ST. GEORGE and THE DRAGON · SILVER 38.61mm

Date	Mintage		Fine	V.F.	E.F.	Unc/abtFDC
1902	256,020		£20	£40	£60	£120/£130
1902	15,123	proof with matt surface			£60	£100/£125
1902	(noted 1999)		- - -	- - -	"abt.F.D.C."	£115
1902	★ Pattern	depicting Edward VII, robed, and on horseback				- - - -
1902	Pattern	similar to the previous entry, struck in gold				- - - -
	★ 1902 Style as Charles I "Tower" (Spinks 1985)					£2,500

CROWNS

Date	Mintage	Fine	V.F.	E.F.	Unc/FDC

GEORGE V
debased silver .500 fineness from 1927
Reverse: ST. GEORGE and THE DRAGON · SILVER 38.61mm

Date	Mintage	Fine	V.F.	E.F.	Unc/FDC
1910	Pattern: flowing interpretation George/Dragon				
1910	Similar but date in exergue reverse (ESC 389)				£3,500
1927	15,030 proofs from the sets			£60	£90/£100
1928	9,034	£30	£60	£90	£125/£175
1928	(noted 2002)			"Virt.BU"	£175
1929	4,994	£30	£60	£90	£125/£175
1930	4,847	£30	£60	£90	£130/£180
1931	4,056	£35	£70	£140	£180/£290
1932	2,395	£50	£75	£150	£200/£300
1932	4 proof		(noted 1986)	"gdEF/FDC"	£950
1933	7,132	£30	£60	£95	£145/£250
1934	932	£300	£500	£1000	£1500/£---
1934	(noted 2001)	---	---	"EF" £825	--/----
1934	8 proof		(Coincraft Cat. '97)		£4000
1935	714,769 incuse edge lettering	£4		£9	£12/£18
1935	Superior strikings,	---	---	in special box	£25/£35
1935	Superior strikings,	---	---	without box	£20/£30
1935	2,500		silver proofs, raised edge lettering		£200/£250
1935	A few .925 silver proof incuse edge lettering				£1750
1935 ★	Some; both incuse and raised, have edge lettering error				
1935	Error edge	£50	£75	£125	£250/£325
1935	30 proof struck in gold raised edge lettering				£12000
1935	A pattern - date in front of horse's head				£15,950
1936	2,473	£60	£100	£200	£300/£350
1936	(noted 2002)	---	"gdVF" £150	----	---/----
1936	3 or 4 proofs are thought to exist			"guesstimate"	£1600

★ correct order of words: DECUS ET TUTAMEN ANNO REGNI

EDWARD VIII
.500 silver 38.61mm

Date				
1936	Unofficial patterns (Hearn)		FDC	£30
1936	(noted 2001)		"FDC"	£35
1936	Sterling silver proofs by Maklouf		FDC	£30
1937	designs similar to George VI		"guesstimate"	£75,000

GEORGE VI
.500 fine silver 38.61mm

Date	Mintage		Fine	V.F.	E.F.	Unc/FDC
1937	418,699	Coronation		£12	£18	£22/£30
1937	26,402	Proofs from the sets			---	£30/£40
1937	Proofs with special frosting (V.I.P.) 0.925 silver					£200/£250
1937	Matt, sand-blasted die, patterns			---	---	/£800

Date	Mintage		Fine	V.F.	E.F.	Abt. Unc/FDC.

GEORGE VI — *Cupro-nickel*

MDCCCLI CIVIUM INDUSTRIA FLORET CIVITAS MCMLI
(1851 By the industry of its people the state flourishes 1951)

1951	1,983,540	Festival of Britain	Prooflike	£4	£6/£8
1951	In box of issue, green or purple			£6	£8/£10
1951	Proofs from the sets (same striking as previous)				£6/£8
1951	Proofs with special frosting	(V.I.P.) 0.925 silver			£150/£200
1951★	Patterns (or special proofs)	(K.B.Coins 1990)			FDC £450
1951	Proofs, error strike on unedged blanks				£150/£250
1951	Matt, sand-blasted die, patterns	---	---		/£800

★ Not to be confused with 'prooflike' issue; the 'specials' have finer edge lettering and are, usually, accompanied by written provenance.

ELIZABETH II

CUPRO-NICKEL 38mm

1953	5,962,621	Equestrian	---	£1	£3	£4/£6
1953	Edge: · AND TRUST ··· UNTO YO (no 'U'):			£20	£30	£40/£50
1953	40,000	Proofs, sets and Maundy			£15	£20/£30
1953★	(K.B.Coins '94)	(Special V.I.P. proofs)				FDC £395
1953	Pattern	All-over frosting, dismal/matt				£600/£700
1953	Large date/Large emblems on cross				---	£350
1960	1,024,038	British Trades Fair		£2	£4	£6/£8
1960	70,000	Polished die specials		---	£5	£9/£16
1960★	(K.B.Coins '94)	(V.I.P. Proof)				FDC £475
1965	19,640,000	Churchill	---	---	50p	75p/£1
1965	(Spink 2000)	Satin finish "special"				FDC £350

★ Frosted detail, highly polished field; not to be confused with 'ordinary' polished die proofs: the 'specials' have finer edge lettering and a written Provenance.

ELIZABETH II
DECIMAL CROWNS 25p

		Selected Unc.	Proof from Set	Silver Proof from/to	Silver Proof Mintage
1972	7,452,000 Silver Wedding	£2	£5	£14/£20	100,000
1977	36,989,000 Silver Jubilee	£2	£5	£14/£20	377,000
1977	Selected coins in RM folder	£4			
1980	Queen Mother's 80th Birthday 9,477,513	£2	£6	£22/£25	83,672
1980	Selected coins in RM folder	£5			
1981	Royal Wedding: 27,360,279	£2	£6	£25/£35	218,142
1981	Selected coins in RM folder	£5			

Smith's Private Pattern Decimals

1, 2, 5 and 10 cents		inverted reverse	£900
1, 2, 5 and 10 cents restrikes		upright reverse	£300

VICTORIA

DECIMAL 'FARTHING' of 1854	1/1000 of £1	a MILLE
1854 (noted 94) "As struck" MODEL MILLE, GOTHIC HEAD,		£125
1854 (noted 1996) "abtVF" £89 "gdVF" £99		- - - -

VICTORIA PATTERNS of 1857   BRITANNIA Reverse   BRONZE

	Legend above Britannia:	Legend below Britannia:	
A)	ONE CENT	MDCCCLVII	16.5mm
B)	HALF FARTHING	ONE CENTIME	17.0mm
C)	TWO CENTS	MDCCCLVII	22.0mm
D)	ONE FARTHING	TWO CENTIMES	22.0mm
E)	FIVE CENTS	MDCCCLVII	27.0mm
F)	DECIMAL HALFPENNY	5 CENTIMES	27.5mm
G)	DECIMAL HALFPENNY	MDCCCLVII	27.0mm
H)	FIVE FARTHINGS	10 CENTIMES	33.5mm
H)	(Noted 1989 about V.F.)	FIVE FARTHINGS	£125
I)	DECIMAL PENNY	ONE TENTH OF A SHILLING	32.5mm
J)	TEN CENTS	ONE TENTH OF A SHILLING	32.5mm

VICTORIA PATTERNS of 1859 DATE BELOW HEAD — BRONZE

K)	HALF DECIMAL PENNY	in wreath oak leaves/acorns	27mm
L)	HALF DECIMAL PENNY	ONE TWENTIETH SHILLING	27mm
M)	ONE DECIMAL PENNY	in wreath oak leaves/acorns	32mm
M)	(Noted 1986 E.F.)	Cupro-nickel and tin	£400
N)		ONE TENTH OF DECIMAL SHILLING A PENNY	32mm
O)		★ DECIMAL PENNY ★ ONE TENTH OF A SHILLING	32mm
O2)		Has larger lettering and date between ornaments	32mm
O2)	(Noted 1986 E.F.)	Nickel-bronze	£250
P)	ONE DECIMAL PENNY	wreath laurel leaves/berries	32mm
Q)	As P)	but wreath half palm leaves, half oak leaves	32mm
R)	ONE DECIMAL PENNY	lion, shield, flags, bee-hive	32mm
S)	DECIMAL PENNY	crown, trident, laurel/oak wreath	32mm

VICTORIA PATTERNS of 1859 SIZE REDUCED — BRONZE

T)	DECIMAL HALF PENNY	23mm	laurel wreath with berries
U)	DECIMAL HALF PENNY	23mm	half laurel, half oak, crown
V)	DECIMAL HALF PENNY	23mm	complete circle of palm leaves
W)	ONE DECIMAL PENNY in exergue	27mm	lion and palm tree
X)	DECIMAL 1 PENNY	27mm	below large trident with dolphins
Y)	ONE PENNY Una and the Lion	27mm	DECIMAL in exergue
Z)	ONE DECIMAL PENNY	27mm	wreath alternating oak & laurel
Z2)	ONE DECIMAL PENNY	27mm	wreath half oak, half laurel
Z3)	Roses, Shamrocks, Thistles around	27mm	ONE DECIMAL PENNY

Coins without date, or without denomination, not listed.

VICTORIA *Silver Patterns 1848 ONE TENTH OF A POUND 27 mm*

1) Trident, wreath of oak leaves, 100 MILLES - ONE DECADE
2) Trident, wreath of oak leaves, 100 MILLES - ONE CENTUM
3) Trident - wreath of oak leaves - ONE FLORIN
4) Royal cypher VR - emblems intertwined - ONE DECADE
4) (noted 1988) ONE DECADE "as struck" £725
5) Royal cypher VR - emblems intertwined - ONE CENTUM
5) (Spink 1988) ONE CENTUM "gdEF" £695
6) Royal cypher VR - emblems intertwined - ONE FLORIN
7) Cruciform shields - rose at centre, below - ONE DIME
Each of the seven with three different obverses (!)
8) Cruciform shields - laureate head - date below
9) Cruciform shields - plain hair binding - date below
10) 1848 Cruciform shields - crowned bust - Godless florin
11) 1851 As 1848 but in Gothic style: the date as mdcccli
Values for GODLESS and GOTHIC florins on page 52

ELIZABETH II — *Decimal Patterns*

1 CENT - 1961 - ER - ONE DECIMAL PENNY - Bronze 20mm
2 CENTS - crown, ornamented trident - 1961 - Bronze 25mm
Set of 1961 comprising 1, 2, 5, 10, 20 and 50 cents sold at Sotheby's 1986 for £2,400 plus buyers premium and VAT

Aluminium quarter penny	Tudor Rose over 1/4	20mm
Bronze half penny	Welsh Dragon over 1/2	17mm
Bronze penny	Scottish Lion, St Andrews Cross	20mm
Bronze two pence	Britannia over large 2	26mm
Cupro-nickel five pence	Three Crowns over 5	23mm
Cupro-nickel ten pence	St George and The Dragon	28mm
Cupro-nickel twenty pence	Gartered Royal Arms	36mm

In 1982, a decimal pattern for 20p dated 1963 @ £1,500
In 1986, full set of decimal patterns dated 1963 @ £4,500
In 1986, uniface set artist's copies at Spink's @ £900

IN 1982 THE WORD 'NEW' WAS DISCONTINUED

BRONZE 17mm   **Half New Penny**   THE ROYAL CROWN

		Selected Unc/Proof			Selected Unc/Proof
1971	1,394,188,250	20p/£2	1979		20p/£2
1971	Double headed	£200	1980		50p/£2
1972	Proof ex-set	---/£5	1981	46,748,000	60p/£2
1973	365,680,000	50p/£2	1982		15p/£2
1974	365,448,000	50p/£2	1983	7,600,000	25p/£2
1975	197,600,000	50p/£2			
1976	412,172,000	50p/£2		From sets	
1977		20p/£2	1984	158,820	£2/£3
1978	59,532,000	25p/£2		Demonetized 31/12/84	

BRONZE 20mm to 1991   **One New Penny**   Plated Steel, magnetic, 1992
A PORTCULLIS WITH CHAINS ROYALLY CROWNED   non-magnetic 1998

		Selected Unc/Proof		Selected Unc/Proof
1971	1,521,666,250	15p/£2	1989	50p/£2
1972	Proof from set	---/£5	1990	50p/£2
1973	280,196,000	£1/£3	1991	50p/£2
1974	330,892,000	£1/£3	1992	£5/£5
1975	221,604,000	£1/£3	Now "magnetic" until 1998	
1976	241,800,000	£1/£3	1992	10p/£2
1977	285,430,000	£1/£3	1993	10p/£2
1978	292,770,000	£1/£3	1994	10p/£2
1979	459,000,000	£1/£3	1995	10p/£2
1980	416,304,000	£1/£3	1996	10p/£2
1981	301,800,000	£1/£3	1997	10p/£2
1982		60p/£2	1998	New portrait
1983	243,002,000	£1/£3	1999	....
1984	154,759,625	£1/£3	2000	....
1985	200,605,245	50p/£2	2001	....
1986	369,989,130	50p/£2	2002	....
1987	499,946,000	50p/£2	2003	.....
1988	793,492,000	50p/£2	2004	

---

         non-magnetic 1998
BRONZE 26mm to 1991   **Two New Pence**   Plated Steel, magnetic, 1992
THE BADGE OF THE PRINCE OF WALES

		Selected Unc/Proof			Selected Unc/Proof
1971	1,454,856,250	15p/£2	1988	419,889,000	50p/£2
1972,	1973, 1974	---/£5	1989	292,093,000	50p/£2
1975	145,545,000	75p/£2	1990		25p/£2
1976	181,379,000	75p/£2	1991		25p/£2
1977	109,261,000	25p/£2	1992		£5/£5
1978	189,658,000	£1/£3	Now "magnetic" until 1998		
1979	260,200,000	30p/£2	1992		25p/£2
1980	408,527,000	25p/£2	1993		25p/£2
1981	353,191,000	30p/£2	1994		25p/£2
1981	Double "tail"	£125	1995		10p/£2
1982	205,000	£4/£2	1996		10p/£2
1983	637,100	£3/£2	1997		10p/£2
1983	with old rev.		1998		New portrait
1984	158,820	£1/£2	1999		....
1985	107,113,000	50p/£2	2000		....
1986	168,967,500	50p/£2	2001		....
1987	218,100,750	50p/£2	2002		....
			2003		.....

1998   Rotated die · authenticated by R.M. - ref: B. Simpson Esq.

Five Pence

23.59mm 1968-1990   18mm 1990 onwards
A THISTLE ROYALLY CROWNED

Selected	Unc/Proof★		Selected	Unc/Proof★	
1968 98,868,250	50p/	--	1989 101,406,000	£1/	£3
1969 119,270,000	75p/	--	1990★	£3/	£4
1970 225,948,525	75p/	--	1990 Smaller/18mm	20p/	£2
1971 81,783,475	75p/	£2	1990 35,000 silver		
1972★	---/	£6	'pair' both sizes		£25
1973★	---/	£6	1990 20,000 piedfort		£30
1974★	---/	£6	1991	20p/	£2
1975 86,550,000	50p/	£2	1992	20p/	£2
1976★	---/	£4	1993	50p/	£3
1977 24,308,000	35p/	£2	1994	50p/	£2
1978 61,000,000	50p/	£3	1995	---/	£2
1979 155,456,000	75p/	£3	1996	---/	£2
1980 220,566,000	£1/	£3	1996 Silver proof		£15
1981★	--/	£6	1997	---/	£2
1982★ 205,000	£5/	£5	1998	---/	£3
1983★ 637,100	£5/	£5	1999	---/	£3
1984★ 158,820	£3/	£5	2000	---/	£3
1985★ 178,375	£3/	£4	2001	---/	---
1986★	£2/	£3	2002	---/	---
1987 48,220,000	£1/	£2	2003		
1988 120,744,610	£1/	£2			

Ten Pence

28.5mm 1968-1990   24.5mm 1990 onwards
CUPRO-NICKEL · A LION PASSANT GUARDANT ROYALLY CROWNED

Selected	Unc/Proof★		Selected	Unc/Proof★	
1968 336,143,250	£1/	--	1990★	£4/	£6
1969 314,008,000	£2/	--	1991★	£4/	£6
1970 133,571,000	£3/	--	1992★	£4/	£6
1971 63,205,000	£3/	£4	Smaller 24.5mm		
1972 Proof from set	--/	£5	1992	£3/	£4
1973 152,174,000	£2/	£4	1992 Silver Proof		
1974 92,741,000	£2/	£4	'pair' both sizes		£30
1975 181,559,000	£2/	£4	1992 Silver Proof		£10
1976 228,220,000	£2/	£4	1992 Piedfort		£50
1977 59,323,000	£2/	£3	1993 ★	£5/	£4
1978 Proof from set	--/	£6	1994 ★	£4/	£4
1979 115,457,000	£2/	£4	1995	£3/	£4
1980 88,650,000	£2/	£4	1996	£2/	£3
1981 3,487,000	£3/	£5	1996 Silver proof		£15
1982★ 205,000	£5/	£6	1997	£2/	£3
1983★ 637,100	£6/	£7	1998 ★	---/	£3
1984★ 158,820	£3/	£4	1999 ★	---/	£3
1985★ 178,375	£3/	£4	2000	---/	£3
1986★	£2/	£3	2001	---/---	
1987★ 172,425	£2/	£3	2002	---/---	
1988★	£2/	£3	2003		
1989★	£3/	£4			

DECIMAL COINAGE
TWENTY PENCE

CUPRO-NICKEL 21.4mm   A DOUBLE ROSE ROYALLY CROWNED

Year	Mintage	Selected Unc/Proof★		Year	Mintage	Selected Unc/Proof★
1982	740,815,000	£1/ £6		1994		£1/ £2
1982	25,000 Piedfort	/£50		1995		50p/ £1
1983	158,463,000	£1/ £5		1996		50p/ £1
1984	65,350,965	£1/ £5		1996	Silver	/£15
1985	74,273,699	£1/ £5		1997		50p/ £1
1986	From the sets	£1/ £5		1998		/ £3
1987	137,450,000	£1/ £5		1999		/ £3
1988	38,038,344	£1/ £4		2000		/ £3
1989	109,128,890	£1/ £4		2001		
1990		£1/ £5		2002		
1991		£1/ £5		2003		
1992		£1/ £4		2004		
1993★★		£1/ £3				

★★ R. Colliass Esq reports, and the Royal Mint confirms, a steel blank intended blank intended for a 1p struck in error with the dies of the of the 1993 20p (source 1995)

CUPRO-NICKEL 30 mm **FIFTY PENCE** 'NEW' DISCONTINUED 1982

Proofs, are those taken from the sets unless otherwise indicated.

Year	Mintage	Selected Unc/Proof		Year	Mintage	Sel.Unc/Proof
1969	188,400,000	£3/£4		1987	172,425	£2/£5
1969	Double 'head'	£150		1988		£3/£5
1970	19,461,000	£2/£5		1989		£3/£5
1971	and 1972	--/£6		1990		£3/£6
1973	89,775,000	£3/--		1991		£5/£9
Proofs	356,616 cased	£4		1992		£4/£5
Piedfort	(about 20)	£2,500		1993		£4/£4
1974	and 1975	--/£5		1992/93 ★★★		£5/£9
1976	43,746,500	£3/£6		Silver ★★★		£30
1977	49,536,000	£3/£6		Piedfort ★★★		£60
1978	72,005,500	£3/£6		Gold ★★★		£500
1979	58,680,000	£3/£6		1994 ex-sets		£3/£6
1980	89,086,000	£3/£6		1995 ex-sets		£4/£6
1981	74,002,000	£2/£4		1996 ex-sets		£3/£6
1981	Double 'tail'	£200		1996 Silver		/£15
1982	51,312,000	£2/£5		1997 ex-sets		£3/£6
1983	62,824,904	£2/£5		1997	new size 27.3mm	
1984	158,820	£2/£5		1997		---/---
1985	679,603	£2/£5		1998		
1986		£2/£5				

1973 (currency and proofs)
EEC Commemoratives

1992/1993 ★★★ Design to commemmorate
Britain's Presidency/Council of Ministers

	Selected Unc./Proof	Uncirc. Folder	Silver Proof	Silver Piedfort	Gold
NEW EFFIGY by Ian Rank-Broadley see page 40					
1994 "D-Day"	£1/£5	£5	£40	£75	£450
1997 10,000 27.3mm New Size	£1/£4	---	£26.75	£50	----
1997 Cased Pairs 30mm and 27.3mm	---/---	---	£47.50	---	----
1998 Traditional Britannia reverse	£2/£3	---	---	---	----
1998 25 Year Commem. of EU · 12 stars	£2/£5	---	£24.95	£45	£249
1998 Pair · Britannia and EU	£5.45/	---	---	---	----
1998 50th Anniversary of N.H.S.	50p/£5	£5	£24.95	£45	£249
1998 Pair · EU and N.H.S.	---/---	---	£49.90	---	----

		Selected Unc./Proof	Uncirc. Folder	Silver Proof	Silver Piedfort	Gold
1999	Traditional Britannia reverse	£2/£3				
2000	150 years Public Libraries	50p/£3	£5	£24.95	£46	£249
2000	Traditional Britannia reverse	£2/£3				
2001	Traditional Britannia reverse	£2/£3				
2002						
2003						
2004						

ONE POUND (One Hundred Pence)

Pale-yellow mixture of metals · 22.5 mm dia. · 3.1 mm thick · has grained (milled) edge, with incuse (struck in) lettering. England and Northern Ireland variants read: DECUS ET TUTAMEN (An Ornament and a Safeguard) first used to prevent the clipping of coins.

Scotland: NEMO ME IMPUNE LACESSIT: (No One Provokes Me with Impunity)

For Wales: PLEIDOL WYF I'M GWALD :   (True Am I to My Country)

ONE POUND (One Hundred Pence)

Date	Mintage		Unc./Proof
1983	434,000,000	Royal Coat of Arms general issue	£3/£5
1983	484,900	Selected general issue in wallet	£6/- -
1983	50,000	Sterling silver (.925) proofs	£25
1983	10,000	Silver Piedfort proofs.	£125
1984	110,000,000	Thistle for Scotland general issue	£2/£5
1984	27,960	Selected general issue in wallet	£6/- -
1984	44,855	Sterling silver (.925) proofs	£20
1984	15,000	Silver Piedfort proofs.	£45
1984/87	Proof set of 4 £1 coins (noted 2001)	"FDC"	£60
1985	178,000,000	Leek for Wales general issue	£3/£5
1985		Selected general issue in wallet	£6/- -
1985	50,000	Sterling silver (.925) proofs	£20
1985	15,000	Silver Piedfort proofs.	£45
1986	Not revealed	Flax Plant for Northern Ireland	£2/£5
		Selected general issue in wallet	£6/- -
1986	50,000	Sterling silver (.925) proofs	£25
1986	15,000	Silver Piedfort proofs.	£45

72 ONE POUND (One Hundred Pence)

Date	Mintage		Unc./Proof
1987		An Oak Tree for general issue	£2/£5
		Selected general issue in wallet	£6/--
1987	50,000	Sterling silver (.925) proofs	£25
1987	15,000	Silver Piedfort proofs.	£45
1988		The Royal Arms of H.M. The Queen	£3/£5
		Selected general issue in wallet	£6/--
1988	50,000	Sterling silver (.925) proofs	£25
1988	15,000	Silver Piedfort proofs.	£45
1989		Re-appearance of the Thistle Pound	£3/£5
		Selected general issue in wallet	£6/--
1989	25,000	Sterling silver (.925) proofs	£20
1989	10,000	Silver Piedfort proofs.	£50
1990		Re-appearance of the Leek Pound	£2/£4
1990	25,000	Sterling silver (.925) proofs	£20
1991		Re-appearance of the Flax Pound	£2/£4
1991	25,000	Sterling silver (.925) proofs	£20
1992		General Issue (Oak Tree)	£2/£4
1992	25,000	Sterling silver (.925) proofs	£20
1993		General Issue · Royal Arms	£2/£4
1993	25,000	Sterling silver (.925) proofs	£30
1993	12,500	Silver Peidfort proofs	£50

| 1984 - 1987 | 4 coin silver proof collection in red leather case | £60 |
| 1984 - 1987 | 4 coin silver piedfort proof collection | £125 |

NEW SERIES   ISSUE PRICE   Selected Unc/Proof

Year	Mintage	Description	Price
1994		Scottish Lion Rampant	£2/ £5
1994	25,000	Sterling silver (.925) proofs	£30
1994	12,500	Silver Piedfort proofs	£50
1994		Presentation folder, nickel-brass	£3/---
1995		Welsh Dragon · nickel-brass:	£3/ £5
		Presentation folder · English text	£4/---
		Presentation folder · text in Welsh	£5/---
1995	25,000	Sterling silver (.925) proofs	£25
1995	12,500	Silver Piedfort proofs	£50
1996		N. Ireland Celtic Cross	£2/ £4
1996		Presentation folder, nickel-brass	£4/---
1996	25,000	Sterling silver (.925) proofs	£25
1996	12,500	Silver Piedfort proofs	£50
1997		English: Three Lions *passant guardant*	£2/ £4
1997		Presentation folder, nickel-brass	£4.50
1997	30,000	Sterling silver (.925) proofs	£25
1997	10,000	Silver Piedfort proofs	£50

The Royal Mint reports a 'rash' of forged £1 coins with inappropriate "sides"

NEW PORTRAIT by Ian Rank-Broadley	Selected Unc/Proof		Uncirc. Folder	Silver Proof	Silver Piedfort	Philatelic (PNCs) Numismatic Covers	
1998 The Royal Arms	£2/	£6	£4.50	£25	£45	30,000 ·	£12.95
1999 Scottish Lion	£2/	£6	£4.50	£25	£45	40,000 ·	£12.95
2000 Welsh Dragon	£2/	£4	£4.50	£25	£50		£12.95
2001 Broighter Collar · N.I.	£2/	£4	£4.50	£26	£50		£12.95
2002 Three Lions *Passant Guardant*	£2/	£4		£26		35,000 ·	£12.95
2003							

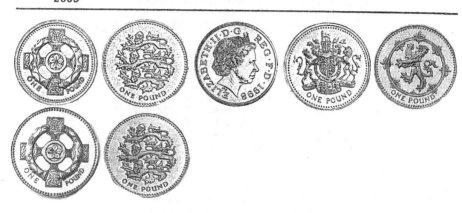

TWO POUNDS
(Issue Price or Selected/Uncirculated Values · 28.4mm · 12 grams)

1986 COMMEMORATING EDINBURGH COMMONWEALTH GAMES

Thistle, Wreath, Cross of St.Andrew	£3	Selected in wallet	£6
125,000 Nickel-brass proofs	£6	58,881 .500 silver	£15
59,779 925 silver proofs	£25	3,277 gold proofs	£200

1989 COMMEMORATING 300th ANNIVERSARY BILL OF RIGHTS
William & Mary. Not for general issue, but still legal tender.

Bill of Rights	£4	Selected in wallet	£5
Claim of Right	£8	Selected in wallet	£10
Pair, as picture, selected, in Official blister-pack			£16
25,000 each Bill and Claim proofs in silver singles			£24
10,000 pairs Bill AND Claim proofs, silver, piedfort, pairs			£90

TWO POUNDS

1994 COMMEMORATING TERCENTENARY of THE BANK OF ENGLAND
Edge: SIC VOS NON VOBIS (Thus you labour but not for yourselves)
Uncirculated £3 · Blister-pack £5 · Proofs from sets £6
Silver proof, 27,957, £25 · Silver Proof Piedfort £50
Gold 'TWO POUNDS' £400 · error not showing value £700

1995 WORLD WAR II · DOVE OF PEACE · edge: IN PEACE GOODWILL
Uncirculated £3 · Blister-pack £4 · Proofs from sets £6
Silver Proof 50,000, £30 · Piedfort, 10,000, £50 · Gold Proof, £375

1995 UNITED NATIONS 50th ANNIVERSARY · 1945 - 1995
Uncirculated £3 · Proof £6 · Folder £5 · Silver Proof, 175,000, £30
Silver Proof Piedfort 10,000 £50 · Gold Proof 17,500 £350

1996 EUROPEAN FOOTBALL CHAMPIONSHIP
Uncirculated £3 · Selected in Folder £5 · Proof £6
Silver Proof 50,000 £27 · Piedfort 10,000 £55 · Gold 2,098 £295
Missing designer's initials (like old-time laces) £9

1997 GENERAL CIRCULATION · FIRST TWO-TONE COIN
Uncirculated £3 · Selected in Folder £6 · Proof £6
Silver Proof (has the outer ring plated with ·999 gold) 40,000 £29
Silver Proof Piedfort 10,000 £50
Gold Proof (using 22 carat red gold outer/yellow gold inner) 2,500 £325

1997 release of TWO-TONE ROYAL MINT TRIAL dated 1994
Descriptive card folder featuring four items: Inner and Outer Blanks;
The Inner combined with Edge Lettered Outer; and the Finished Coin · £20

1998 BRITISH INDUSTRY · edge: STANDING on the SHOULDERS of GIANTS
New effigy of H.M. The Queen by Ian Rank-Broadley Rev. by Bruce Rushin
Commenced general circulation on Monday 15th June, 1998
Uncirculated £4 · Proof £6 · Folder £6 · Silver Proof 25,000, £29
Silver Proof Piedfort 10,000 £50
Gold Proof (using 22 carat red gold outer/yellow gold inner) 2,500 £325

1999 RUGBY WORLD CUP TOURNAMENT · edge: RUGBY WORLD CUP 1999
Aerial representation of Stadium, Ball and Goal Posts
Uncirculated £3 · Proof £6 · Folder £6 · Silver Proof 25,000, £29
Silver Proof Piedfort · Colour Producing Holography · 10,000 £50
Gold Proof (using 22 carat red gold outer/yellow gold inner) 2,000 £325

2000 BRITISH INDUSTRY · edge: STANDING on the SHOULDERS of GIANTS
Bruce Rushkin's reverse design repeated

2001 MARCONI · edge: WIRELESS BRIDGES THE ATLANTIC · MARCONI 1901
Decorative Radio Waves emanating from a spark of electricity · Robert Evans
Uncirculated £3 · Folder £7 · Silver Proof 25,000, £29
Gold Proof (using 22 carat red gold outer/yellow gold inner) 2,500 £295

2001 BRITISH INDUSTRY · edge: STANDING on the SHOULDERS of GIANTS
Bruce Rushkin's reverse design repeated

2002 BRITISH INDUSTRY · edge: STANDING on the SHOULDERS of GIANTS
Bruce Rushkin's reverse design repeated

2002 COMMONWEALTH GAMES · SET OF FOUR COINS
edge: SPIRIT OF FRIENDSHIP, MANCHESTER 2002
Uncirculated Set in Folder £15 · Proof Set £25 · Display Proof £32.50
Silver Proof (has the outer ring plated with ·999 gold) 10,000 £97.50
Reverse design by Matthew Bonaccorsi
The design features a cameo of each of the United Kingdom flags

---

FIVE POUNDS ISSUE PRICES

Legal Tender for £5 · 38.61mm · 28.28 grams

1990 COMMEMORATING THE QUEEN MOTHER's 90th BIRTHDAY
Interlaced Es - Rose and Thistle - Uncirculated £8
Pack £10 · Silver Proofs 56,102, £38 · Gold Proofs 2,500, £600

1993 THE CORONATION ANNIVERSARY 1953/1993
Queen's 1953 portrait encircled by mounted trumpeters/swords/sceptres
Selected Unc. £7 · Official Pack £10 · Cupro-nickel Proofs £9
Silver Proofs 100,000 £32 · Gold Proofs 2,500 £650

1996 COMMEMORATING H.M. THE QUEEN'S 70th BIRTHDAY
Edge: VIVAT REGINA ELIZABETHA
Selected Unc. £7 · Official Pack £10 · Cupro-nickel Proofs £12
Silver Proofs 70,000 £32 · Gold Proofs 2,127 £650

1997 COMMEMORATING THE GOLDEN WEDDING
Princess Elizabeth to Lieutenant Phillip Mountbatten 20th Nov. 1947
Selected Unc. £7 · Official Pack £10 · Cupro-nickel Proofs £12
Silver Proofs 75,000 £32 · Gold Proofs 2,750 £650

1998 COMMEMORATING 50th BIRTHDAY H.R.H. The Prince of Wales
New Effigy of H.M. The Queen by Ian Rank Broadley · Rev. by Michael Noakes
Selected Unc. £7 · Official Pack £10 · Cupro-nickel Proofs £12
Silver Proofs 35,000 £32 · Gold Proofs 2,000 £600

1999 PRINCESS DIANA COMMEMORATIVE · July 1st, 1999
Selected Unc. £7 · Official Pack £10 · PNC postmark 1/1/99 £16
Cu-nickel Proof £12 · Silv. Proof 350,000 £32 · Gold Proof 7,500 £595

1999 · 2000 MILLENNIUM · edge: What's Past is Prologue ("The Tempest")
Obverse dated 1999 · Selected Unc. £7 · Official Pack £10
Cupro-nickel Proof £12 · Silver Proof 100,000 £35 · Gold Proof 2,500 £600

FIVE POUNDS

2000 MILLENNIUM (repeat of 1999 except for obverse date)
Obverse dated 2000 · Selected Unc. £7 · Official Pack £10
Cupro-nickel Proof £12 · Silver Proof 100,000 £35 · Gold Proof 2,500 £600

2000 COMMEMORATING THE QUEEN MOTHER'S 100th BIRTHDAY
Selected Unc. £6 · Official Pack £10 · PNC £15.95
Silver Proof £35 · Silver Piedfort Proof 20,000 £68 · Gold 3,000 £495
Proof Crown and £5 note with prefix QM10-0 £50

2001 VICTORIAN ANNIVERSARY CROWN (£5)
Selected Unc. £6 · Official Pack £10 · PNC £15.95
Silver Proof £35 · Gold 3,500 £525

2002 GOLDEN JUBILEE · edge: AMOR POPULI PRAESIDIUM REG
"THE LOVE OF THE PEOPLE IS THE QUEEN'S PROTECTION"
Selected Unc. £6 · Official Pack £10 · PNC £15.95 · PNC + Banknote £44.95
Silver Proof 75,000 £35 · Gold 5,502 £525

PROOF and Uncirculated SETS

	F. D. C. from / to

GEORGE IV

1826	140 sets	(11) Farthing to five pounds	£17,000/£20,000
	(noted 2000)	the above plus Maundy	£18,500

WILLIAM IV

1831	145 sets	(14) Maundy replaces £5	£12,500/£16,500
	Silver only	(8) (Spink 1988) E.F. £4,400	- - - - - -

VICTORIA

1839	300 sets	(15) in spade shaped case which includes:	
	(May 2001)	the Una-and-The-Lion gold £5	£25,300
1853	460	(16) Quarter-farthing to Gothic 5/-	£20,000/£25,000
1853	(Cooke 2001)		£24,500
1887	797 sets	(11) unofficial cases	3d to £5	£4,500/ £5,500
1887	287 sets		3d to 5/-	£750/ £950
1893	773 sets	(10) rarely intact	3d to £5	£4,500/ £6,500
1893	Short set of six silver coins		3d to 5/-	£900/ £1,200

EDWARD VII

1902	8,066 sets	(13) Maundy 1d to £5 (matt)	£1,000/ £1,500
1902	7,057 sets	(11) Maundy 1d to sovereign	£400/ £550

GEORGE V

1911	2,812 sets	(12) Maundy 1d to £5	£2,000 £2,500
1911	(noted 1999)	(12) "FDC in case of issue, fabulous"	£2,250
1911	952 sets	(10) Maundy 1d to sovereign	£600/ £750
1911	2,241 sets	(8) Maundy penny to half-crown	£250/ £350
1927	15,030 sets	(6) 3d to crown (noted 2001)	£240
1927	As preceeding entry in official case (noted 2001)		£285

GEORGE VI

1937	5,501 sets	(4) Half-sovereign to £5	£1,500/£1,800
1937	26,402 sets	(15) Farthing to crown + Maundy	£90/ £120
1950	17,513 sets	(9) Farthing to half-crown	£50/ £65
1951	20,000 sets	(10) Farthing to crown	£50/ £75

ELIZABETH II

1953	40,000 sets	(10) Farthing to crown (5/-)	£40/ £60
1953	★ A large number of sets in plastic wallet (9)		£8/ £10
1968	★ Decimal souvenir sets, mixed dates in folder		£1/ £3
1970	750,000 Last Sterling ½d to 2/6d + medallion		£10/ £19

★ non-proof, selected currency coins
(noted 2000 John Satin) plastic set with 1 + B "unc" £10

		FDC from/to			FDC from/to
1971 350,000 (6) ★ half to 50p		£10/£12	1981 100,300 (6) ★ half to 50p		£10/£12
1972 150,000 (7) ★ plus Crown		£10/£12	1982 2,500 (4) half-sov to £5		£750
1973 100,000 (6) ★ half to EEC 50p	£7/ £9		1982 106,800 (7) ★ plus new 20p		£5/£10
1974 100,000 (6) ★ half to 50p		£6/£10	1982 205,000 (7) uncirc in folder		£3/£5
1975 100,000 (6) ★ half to 50p		£7/ £9	1983 12,500 (3) half-sov, sov, £2		£00
1976 100,000 (6) ★ half to 50p		£7/ £9	1983 107,800 (8) ★ plus 20p & £1		£8/£14
1977 193,000 (7) ★ Jubilee Crown	£10/£14		1983 637,100 (8) uncirc in folder		£5/£6
1978 88,100 (6) ★ half to 50p		£12/£16	1984 7,095 (3) half-sov, sov, £5		£600
1979 81,000 (6) ★ half to 50p		£12/£18	1084 125,000 (8) ★ Scottish £1		£8/£14
1980 10,000 (4) half-sov to £5		£650	1984 158,820 uncirc in folder		£5/£6
1981 5,000 (9) ½p to gold £5		£600	1985 (4) half-sov to £5		£650
1981 2,500 (2) Crown & Sov.	£90/£140				

PROOF and Uncirculated SETS

ISSUE PRICE

1985	125,000 (7)	
	★ 1p to Welsh £1	
	in blue leatherette case	£18.75
	in de-luxe red leather case	£25.75
	(7) Uncirc in folder	£4.75
1986	125,000 (8)	
	★ N.I. £1 + C/wealth £2	
	in blue leatherette case	£21.25
	in de-luxe red leather case	£28.25
	(8) Uncirc in folder	£7.95
1987	125,000 (7)	
	★ 1p to English Oak £1	
	in blue leatherette case	£18.95
	in de-luxe red leather case	£25.95
	(7) Uncirc in folder	£5.25
1988	125,000 (7)	
	★ 1p to Royal Arms £1	
	in blue leatherette case	£18.95
	in de-luxe red leather case	£25.95
	(7) Uncirc in folder	£5.25
1989	125,000 (8)	
	★ 1p to 'Orange' £2 x 2	
	in blue leatherette case	£22.95
	in de-luxe red leather case	£29.95
	(8) Uncirc in folder	£5.75
	Boy/Girl Baby Packs in Blue/Pink	£9.95
1990	100,000 (8)	
	★ 1p, (both 5p), 50p to Welsh £1 :	
	in blue leatherette case	£21.95
	in de-luxe red leather case	£28.95
	(8) Uncirc in folder	£6.25
	Boy/Girl Baby Packs in Blue/Pink	£9.95
1991	100,000 (7)	
	★ 1p, to N.I. £1	
	in blue leatherette case	£23.50
	in de-luxe red leather case	£30.60
	(8) Uncirc in folder	£7.10
	Baby Packs	£11.20
	L.s.d. set (dated 1967)	£14.25
1992	100,000 (9)	
	★ 1p, (10p x 2), (50p x 2) to £1	
	in blue leatherette case	£27.50
	in de-luxe red leather case	£34.50
	(9) Uncirc in folder	£8.75
	Wedding/Baby Packs each	£13.95
1993	100,000 (8)	
	★ 1p to £5	
	in blue leatherette case	£28.75
	in de-luxe red leather case	£35.50
	(8) Uncirc 1p to £1 (50p x 2)	£8.75
	Wedding/Baby Sets each	£13.95
1994	100,000 (8)	
	★ 1p to £1	
	in blue leatherette case	£24.75
	in de-luxe red leather case	£32.50
	(8) Uncirc in folder	£8.75
	Wedding/Baby Sets each	£13.95

ISSUE PRICE

1995	100,000 (8)	
	★ 1p to £1	
	in blue leatherette case	£24.75
	in de-luxe red leather case	£32.50
	(8) Uncirc in folder	£8.75
	Baby Gift Set	£13.95
	Wedding Collection	£14.95
1996	100,000	
	(9) ★ 1p to £5	
	in blue leatherette case	£29.75
	in de-luxe red leather case	£37.50
	(8) 1p to £1 in folder	£9.50
	Wedding/Baby Gift each	£14.95
	LSD mixed/Decimal 1996 set	£25.00
1997	100,000	
	(10) ★ 1p to £5 (50p x 2)	
	in blue leatherette case	£32.50
	in de-luxe red leather case	£39.50
	(9) 1p to £2 (50p x 2)	£10.95
	Wedding/Baby Gift each	£14.95
1998	100,000	
	(10) ★ 1p to £5 (50p x 2)	
	in blue leatherette case	£33.00
	in de-luxe red leather case	£40.00
	(9) 1p to £2 (50p x 2)	£10.95
	Wedding/Baby Gift each	£14.95
1999	100,000	
	(9) 1p to £5 proofs	
	in blue leatherette case	£33.95
	in de-luxe red leather case	£39.95
	(8) 1p to £2 uncirculated	£10.95
	Wedding/Baby Gift each	£14.95
2000	100,000	
	(10) ★ 1p to £5 (50p x 2)	
	Standard Proof Set	£29.95
	De-luxe Proof Set	£39.95
	Executive (10,000)	£69.95
	(9) 1p to £2 uncirculated	£11.50
	Wedding/Baby Gift each	£15.95
2001	100,000	
	(10) ★ 1p to £5 (50p x 2)	
	Standard Proof Set	£33.50
	All occasion Gift Proof Set	£42.50
	De-luxe Proof Set	£47.50
	Executive (10,000)	£74.50
	(9) 1p to £2 uncirculated	£13.75
	Wedding/Baby Gift each	£17.50
2002	100,000	
	(9) ★ 1p to £5	
	(9) Standard Proof Set	£31.95
	(9) Gift Proof Set	£39.95
	(8) Wedding/Baby Gift Sets	£17.50
	(9) De-luxe Proof Set	£45.50
	Executive (10,000)	£69.95
	(8) 1p to £2 uncirculated	£13.95
	Baby Gift £5 note and coin	£27.50

A "good" coin is so worn that most of the detail has disappeared. These are not featured: only very rare specimens have any value.

FINE A coin worn by considerable use, but still retaining clear lettering and some of the finer detail (hair, for example, not just a 'parting').

V.F. The highest parts of a VERY FINE coin will show signs of its having been circulated. It must, however, possess a pleasing appearance devoid of disfiguring marks.

E.F. An EXTREMELY FINE coin is almost perfect; close examination revealing traces of wear to the highest parts.

Unc. UNCIRCULATED - unworn, as struck by the mint.

PROOF is not a measure of condition, but a description of the method of manufacture. Certain exceptions apart; the field ("unprinted" part) will possess a mirror-like polish; the inscription, legend, or other design, will have a "frosted" appearance; the whole having an effect of great beauty which the smallest scratch will impair.

Excepting rare coins, the value of which is determined by the fact that nothing better is available, to be "collectable" a coin should possess (at least) the requirements of FINE given above. The 'head' should not be worn to a silhouette. The grading should never be qualified by "for its age": a FINE coin of 1800 should be no more worn than a FINE one of 1900 despite the hundred years age difference. The presence of ALL THE ORIGINAL DETAIL but with the highest parts barely flattened (new but 'shop-soiled') would be considered EXTREMELY FINE. Even uncirculated specimens will vie for honours according to freedom from mint bag-marks, brilliance etc., until the rare title of F.D.C. (fleur de coin) is awarded.

MARKETING

It is generally accepted that for the majority of coins a dealer's buying price is about 50% of his/her selling price. The dealer, in effect, is out-of-pocket until a buyer is found. A different 'deal' can be made where the coin is much sought after, particularly if the dealer has a customer in mind. Auction houses attract groups of buyers: collectors and dealers. Advertising, as you would to sell any other commodity, should stress any variety e.g. Obv.3 + Rev.B rather than a bare coin-date-condition. See, also, footnotes on pages 15 and 16.

CLEANING and POLISHING

A dealer's or auctioneer's list will sometimes indicate that a coin has been cleaned; a lower price results: the lesson should be clear. Cleaning diminishes value; polishing will TOTALLY DESTROY.

V.A.T. REGULATIONS: all coins less than 100 years old, whether or not they are legal tender, when supplied by VAT registered persons, are taxable at the present Standard Rate.